VEHICLE RECOVERY

VEHICLE RECOVERY

A practical manual for the heavy-vehicle driver, fleet operator and recovery specialist

R. J. GRICE

With illustrations by Steve Palmer

NEWNES—BUTTERWORTHS
LONDON—BOSTON
Sydney-Wellington-Durban-Toronto

THE BUTTERWORTH GROUP

United Kingdom	Butterworth & Co (Publishers) Ltd London: 88 Kingsway, WC2B 6AB
Australia	Butterworths Pty Ltd Sydney: 586 Pacific Highway, NSW 2067 Also at Melbourne, Brisbane, Adelaide and Perth
Canada	Butterworth & Co (Canada) Ltd Toronto: 2265 Midland Avenue, Scarborough, Ontario, M1P 4S1
New Zealand	Butterworths of New Zealand Ltd Wellington: 26–28 Waring Taylor Street, 1
South Africa	Butterworth & Co (South Africa) (Pty) Ltd Durban: 152–154 Gale Street
USA	Butterworth (Publishers) Inc Boston: 19 Cummings Park, Woburn, Mass.01801

First published by Newnes-Butterworths, 1977

© Butterworth & Co (Publishers) Ltd 1977

ISBN 0 408 00264 8

Typeset by Butterworths Litho Preparation Department

Printed in England by Butler & Tanner Ltd

PREFACE

Nowadays, Vehicle Recovery is a very important business; it is even almost respectable. It most certainly makes a large contribution to the smooth running of our roads while many operators have been able to use their skills to save life.

At last, it seems as though we have entered a new age in the art of vehicle recovery. This is not to say, however, that the days have gone altogether when a mechanic or petrol pump attendant is called off the job to attend to a breakdown, equipped with a few antique chains and shackles.

One is still able to observe a breakdown crew, sometimes even a well equipped breakdown crew, attacking a casualty with more enthusiasm than knowledge; which is probably where the term 'wrecker' originated.

The purpose of this book is to help refine the art of Vehicle Recovery, or at least gather together and set out the basic principles so that a novice can come to grips with the practical problems and perhaps to encourage the older hands to extend their repertoire.

R. J. GRICE

"Then said another with a long drawn sigh,
My clay with long oblivion is gone dry.
But fill me with the old familiar juice.
Methinks, I might recovery bye and bye"

Rubaiyat of Omar Khayyam
(E. Fitzgerald)

CONTENTS

Chapter 1

PROFITABILITY

To some people profit is a very rude word indeed. Nevertheless, profit is the basic motive for setting up a Recovery Operation.

No one in his right mind would question the value of a deep sea salvage tug; yet these maritime Recovery Vehicles lurk—on full stand-by—at, or near the danger spots of the world and at a very great cost. This cost can only be recovered by arriving at the 'scene' first (a close second is bad for business) with sufficient equipment to effect a rescue. No one gets paid if the casualty sinks. It is a cut and thrust business, paid by results, with no comfortable subsidy from a handy ship repair yard.

Profitability, however, can be shared by two sides. What customer can fail to be delighted if his truck, complete with cargo, can be put on the road again, without having the radiator stove in, within a couple of hours of the accident happening, for a bill less than £100. It could have taken twice as long, suffered considerable damage while the load waited several more hours for a replacement truck to come from distant parts.

For every hour added to a job, the bill will be that much higher. Even so, it is a negligible amount when set against the price and inconvenience of a bent chassis member, torn spring hanger and the like.

Profit is made with brains, not brawn. The object then is:

1. To earn a crust by Recovering Vehicles, and
2. To add a bit of jam by doing it properly.

(Above left, facing page) *Harvey Frost 'Atlas 12' hydraulic recovery crane with 12 ton working capacity mounted on an AEC Militant chassis. This heavy duty unit is suitable only for six or eight wheelers*

(Above, right facing) *This well-equipped recovery vehicle uses the Holmes 750 crane mounted on a Ford D series chassis and is built by Crane Fruehauf Service and Equipment Ltd*

(Centre, facing) *Note the uncluttered layout of this TFL recovery unit with T750 crane, on a Ford D1000 chassis*

(Below, facing) *A tricky problem. This articulated tanker has overturned in a narrow country lane, leaving no space for a direct pull to right the casualty—a case for snatch blocks and ground anchors*

(Above) *Dangerous cargo. A recovery operation of this sort calls for caution, forethought, and close cooperation with the fire service*

(Below) *All goes well, though. Use of the right gear and recovery techniques brings the casualty out of the trees, the resultant rearward pull on the tractor unit being achieved by bringing to bear two separate tackles, one to the recovery vehicle, and one to a tree*

Chapter 2

PRIORITIES

In graphical form, your priorities could look something like *Figure 1*.

From *Figure 1* you will see that this is a question of choosing the correct priorities—the matter of speed and achievement, and the damage sustained. The answer becomes easier with a better understanding of equipment and methods. For example, if you are called upon to save life or limb, speed is of vital importance. Five minutes gained in these circumstances are perhaps worth a twisted chassis.

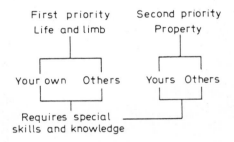

Figure 1

If, on the other hand, life is not involved, three hours saved through rushed and sloppy work can never be equated with the resulting damage. Usually, however, it is a simple equation. Half an hour extra to select the correct chain, and to think about an alternative method to arrange chafing pads are well worthwhile when set against even the smallest dent in bodywork.

Question: How much does an extra half-hour of time cost?
£2? £5?

Question: How much does it cost to hammer out a bodywork dent, prime, paint and polish?
£10? £20?

Another question. Which method is more likely to please your customer?

Remember, that extra cost may be the difference between profit and loss, it could well be the jam mentioned earlier. What's more, you might even get more business from a satisfied client.

Chapter 3

THE TOOLS

It is a fact that if a recovery vehicle were to carry *all* the equipment necessary for every possible job, a very large trailer would be required. Fortunately, however, the brain comes into its own. This is the first and very best tool. Used properly the most difficult jobs can be tackled with limited equipment. On the other hand, give any amount of equipment to a fool and nothing but trouble results.

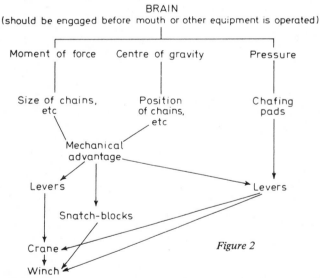

Figure 2

If recovery were a nice, warm, deskbound job a chart could be drawn which would please even the most enthusiastic adepts of Critical Path Analysis in order to select a particular tool for a particular job. A rather more simple chart has been drawn in *Figure 2*, not for practical use, but just as a guide. A more practical method is to use a Memory Aid, like this one from Rudyard Kipling—

'I keep six honest working men,
(They taught me all I knew),
Their names are What and Why and When,
And How and Where and Who'

We will now take a look at the chart. This should not be taken too seriously. It does however make the point that the tools are used after—long after—the brain has weighed up and analysed the theoretical tools of moments of Force, Centre of Gravity, Pressure, etc.

So we arrive at the scene of a breakdown—it's early Monday morning, Winter, and raining. One may be excused for wondering why the devil we're bothering with all this theoretical nonesense. Surely it is just a matter of the three P's—Pile in, Pull out and Park it. However, this book is designed to put the case for the other, more scientific, 'commonsense' approach.

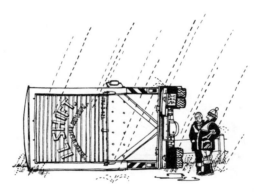

Figure 3

The first thing to do is to decide what tool to use. Suppose that we are confronted with an overturned truck, a four wheeler, say, and just to make our day, it has ended up as shown in *Figure 3*.

'An empty furniture van.'

'How did it get that way?'

It got that way because its Centre of Gravity acted outside of its wheel-track and . . . it fell over. Let us examine this Centre of Gravity more closely.

CENTRE OF GRAVITY

This is the point at which the whole weight of our object is acting vertically downwards. The point, one might say, of balance.

Consider a matchbox (*Figure 4*). Being of regular shape, the Centre of Gravity will lie at the junction of its three axes—in the middle, if you prefer. Look at one side, the Centre of Gravity is 'working' to keep the matchbox firmly on the table—it is now said to be *Stable*—or, in a state of *Stable Equilibrium*.

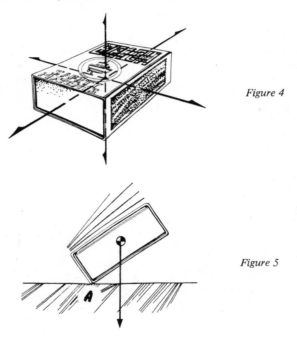

Figure 4

Figure 5

Tilt the matchbox (*Figure 5*). It won't stay that way on its own, due to the fact that its C of G—still in its original position—is 'working' about point A and thus trying to pull back to a stable position—back, in fact, to square one.

Try again, this time with an even greater degree of tilt. Again, the C of G is working about point A, but in the opposite direction, to try and get into a state of Stable Equilibrium.

So, back to our truck. A few seconds before the accident it was like *Figure 6*, with its C of G nicely pointing at the ground between the four wheels. Just as it was designed to do in fact. Then some external force came along and caused it to tilt (*Figure 7*) and ruined everything. Our truck is now *Unstable*, as the C of G is working about the edge of the tyres to reach a stable position—flat on its side.

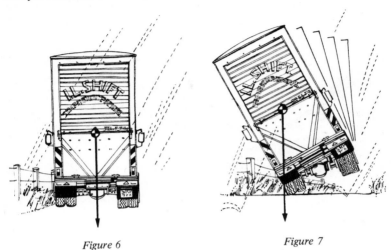

Figure 6   Figure 7

Note that if the C of G had been higher, for example, if it was loaded, the tilt would have been much less before reaching the unstable position. You may have noticed that words like 'acting about' the tyre edge, or point A have been used. Well, a weight on its own will do nothing except sit. It has potential but no action and in this case the missing ingredient is . . . distance.

Just to keep our feet on the ground, don't forget that at the roadside it's still a wet Monday morning and the truck is still on its side. So we must now consider *The Moment of Force*.

THE MOMENT OF FORCE

Quite simply, a Moment of Force about a point (*always* about a point), is weight (or force) multiplied by the distance away from the turning point of that weight or force. Look at it this way: A spanner, 12 in long, with a weight (or force) of, say 20 lb hanging on the end, is applying a Moment of Force of 12 inches × 20 pounds force = 240 lbf.in *about* the centre of the nut (*Figure 8*). This, of course, is why spanners are sometimes more convenient than fingers.

Again, consider a common or garden see-saw (*Figure 9*). The see-saw has tilted because a weight of 100 lbf was placed on one side, 4 ft away from the pivot. Thus, a Moment of Force of 100 lb × 4 ft = 400 lbf.ft has been applied. (Note that the units of moments of force are: lbf.in; lbf.ft, kilogramme.metres, or whatever, as long as it is weight multiplied by distance).

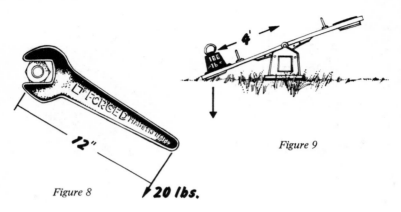

Figure 9

Figure 8

In order to get the see-saw level again, or balanced, it is necessary to apply a Moment of Force equal to 400 lbf.ft on the other side of the pivot or fulcrum. Now suppose that the only weight available is one of 50 lb—no problem, we don't want weight—merely a moment. In this case one of 400 lbf.ft; therefore, by cancelling out in the time honoured method we find that we are required to place the 50 lb weight at a distance of 8 ft from the fulcrum and we have a balance.

So there we are, to the left-hand side of the fulcrum we have 400 lbf.ft which exactly balances the right-hand side of the fulcrum. Now, back to our truck—still on its side.

This is the time to relax and consider the situation.

Question 1. What (remember R. Kipling?) is the weight of the truck? Two tons? four? five? The driver might know. If he doesn't and the truck is empty, the unladen weight is painted on the side of the cab. For the sake of our exercise and to keep it easy, say the weight is four tons dead.

Question 2. Where is the Centre of Gravity? Where, if you were able, would you place a brick under the truck so that the whole thing balanced on this one brick? At A or B or at C in *Figure 10*? Consider the weight of the engine, the gearbox, the axles and the bodywork, try in your mind to balance one against the other and arrive at this single point. Perhaps you will decide that A is the best position. You could be right.

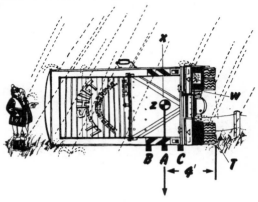

Figure 10

Question 3. How far is A from the point of action—the pivot or *fulcrum*. The fulcrum, about which all the forces balance, is, in this case, the edge of the tyre. How far? Well pace it out—*you* put your mental brick there in the first place. Is it four feet? We'll settle for that, then.

We can now work out what force is holding the truck down (by now it could be the weight of snow) *about* the edge of its tyres. Now do a quick revision. The C of G is acting downwards at A. That is, the whole weight of the truck is concentrated on the line AX̄. The actual C of G is likely to be at Z and the whole weight of the truck, all four tons of it, is acting downwards at A. Therefore, we have a Moment of Force of 4 tons × 4 feet, that is, 16 tonf.ft acting about the edge of the tyres, T.

This means that we must exert a force greater, but only just greater, than 16 tonf.ft to get the truck back on its feet. This is just dandy, but first we must conjure up 16 tonf.ft.

Now, just suppose that we were to wrap a chain around the axle at point W and attach the winch cable thereto and pull in a horizontal direction. How much winch effort will be required?

Look at the diagram in *Figure 11*. Knowing that on average, a truck is about 7½ feet wide, we can attach our chain at a point roughly 6 ft from the fulcrum. Let's simplify the diagram a little: T, we agree, is the fulcrum, as previously worked out.

We have a force of 16 tonf.ft working on the right-hand side (l.h.s.) of T. Again, we agreed that we must have an equal force operating on the r.h.s. of the fulcrum. To help matters along, we know that we have

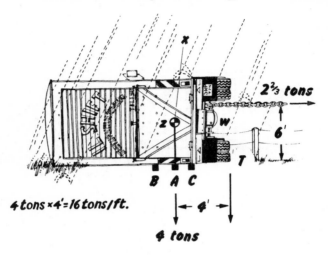

Figure 11

a lever (it used to be an axle) 6 ft long. Therefore, we must exert a winch pull of E tons on this lever to equal the force on the other side. Put it this way:

6 ft × E tons = 16 ton.ft

$$\text{therefore, E tons} = \frac{16 \text{ ton.ft}}{6 \text{ ft}} = 2\tfrac{2}{3} \text{ tons}$$

Just check up on this, the left hand side must balance the right hand side, i.e. $2\tfrac{2}{3}$ tons × 6 ft should equal 4 tons × 4 ft, and it does, both equal 16 ton.ft.

From the above calculations we have found that a winch pull of just a couple of ounces more than $2\tfrac{2}{3}$ tons will pull the truck upright. On the face of it, it appears that if we select chain of at least $2\tfrac{2}{3}$ ton safe working load we can wrap it round the axle, couple up and make with the winch. There is just one snag, however. When walking around the truck, you may have noticed that this particular truck had two axles—one, so to speak, at each end—and so far have been, in the pouring rain, talking about attaching a chain to one of them. This is the classic case of there being at least two sides to a question. Let us have a look at the problem from 'the other side'. From the new diagram (*Figure 12*) point W_1 is clearly visible, as is point T. However, is someone started making with the winch with the chain at W_1 there would be a frightful clatter. For one thing, the back end of the truck would come round to meet us, with a fair chance of twisting the chassis.

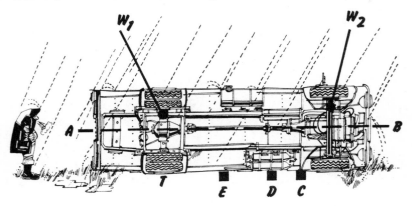

Figure 12

'All very well' you might say, 'no one but an idiot would try that anyway, *I'd* put a chain round the other axle at the point W_2'; and so would most people. However, the two chains will have to meet at some place, if only because one winch cable is available. The point where the two chains join is very important, for two reasons. Firstly, we want a nice, clean movement without any sliding of one end before the other and, secondly, the tension in the chains should be more or less equal.

Figure 13

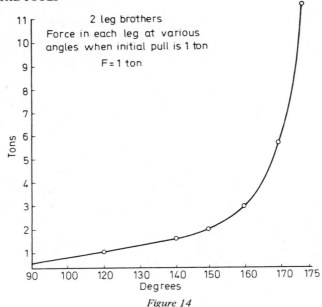

Figure 14

WEIGHT TAKEN BY EACH LEG OF CHAIN

Winch pull	Angle Between Chains (Degrees)								
	90	100	120	130	140	150	160	170	175
1 ton	-	-	1	1.2	1.5	1.9	2.9	5.75	11.5 ton
20 cwt	14	16	20	24	30	38	58	115	142 cwt
	10° jump						5° jump		

The first reason involves our old friend the Centre of Gravity. As we established from last time, this lies on the centre line of the truck, somewhere along the line AB—but where?

Look around and see if you can find the mental brick that was used last time and, again, place it under where you think the truck will balance; at C, D or E. Considering the weight of the engine, the gearbox and the rear axle, you might be inclined to think that D is the best place, and again, you could well be right. Take a bird's eye view of the situation. The C of G is at D, so, ideally, the two chains should be joined at D (*Figure 13*). If they are joined at any other position, the truck will slide either one way or the other. If your estimation is wrong it will now be revealed, so adjust the chains a little until you get it right. At this stage, we should realise that there are more ways than one of joining chains; you can do it at K or at L.

We already know that we need a $2\frac{2}{3}$ ton line pull on the winch and, for reasons that will be explained later, you need much stronger chains if you join at K than if you joined at L. In fact, a $2\frac{2}{3}$ ton line pull at K could result in a force of 16 tons being taken by each of the chains.

Back at the roadside we're ready to go—or are we? Almost, but not quite. Take another walk around and examine the chains that have been wrapped around the axle—let's do the job properly and examine the whole set up on those chains. If the chains are joined at K, they have, say, an angle of 170° between them. Now read off, from *Figure 14*, the force exerted on each chain.

The result is surprising; 16 tons on *each* chain. As a result of applying a force of $2\frac{2}{3}$ tons on the winch cable, we have immediately pushed the load up to 16 tons. Where, one is entitled to ask, does the extra load come from? This extra load does not help right the truck, and it is doing nothing but trying to join the front axle to the back axle—which can be detrimental to the chassis.

The graph in *Figure 14* shows how rapidly the strain goes up as the angle increases. For example, if you have 5 tons winching power, multiply the figures by 5 and adjust the size of the chain that you are using accordingly.

Figure 15

Side view of link

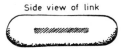

Figure 16

Before going any further, take a very close look at the way a chain is wrapped around, say, the rear axle casing as in *Figure 15*. Let us assume, for the moment (being wildly optimistic) we have a high quality chain and that you have chosen an angle of 160° between the chains, giving (from the table) 3 tons load for each 1 ton of pull on the winch; we want $2\frac{2}{3}$ tons pull and so there will be $2\frac{2}{3} \times 3 = 8$ tons being taken by the chain. Now this chain, being of very high quality is made of material of $\frac{5}{8}$ in.

Take time to examine one such link and measure with your eye the bearing surface. A half size link is illustrated in *Figure 16*. The shaded part is the bit that actually touches the axle casing. As shown, the

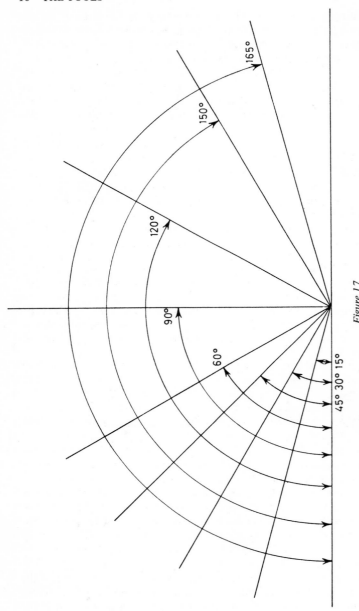

Figure 17

bearing surface is about ¾ in long, about $\frac{1}{16}$ wide = ¾ × $\frac{1}{16}$ = $\frac{3}{64}$ of a square inch in bearing area. Now, count how many links are actually in full contact with the casing. If it is as many as three you're doing well, possibly more like two-and-a-bit, which gives a total bearing area of 2½ × $\frac{3}{64}$ ≃ $\frac{7}{64}$ of a square inch. With 8 tons strain on the chain and with $\frac{5}{32}$ of a square inch to receive it we have a total pressure of 73 tons per square inch! This brings us to the question of *pressure*. Most recovery damage is caused by the lack of recognition that pressure exists at all.

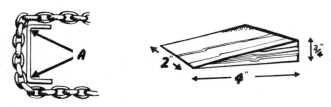

Figure 18   Figure 19

There is one common way in which pressure can ruin a perfectly good job and cost hundreds of pounds (cash). A chain is wrapped around a chassis, pulling in the direction indicated in the sketch (*Figure 18*), with, say, a 5 ton load on the chain. Notice that the only point of contact between the chain and the chassis is at A. The bearing area will be about 1 in × $\frac{1}{16}$ in = $\frac{1}{16}$ of a square inch. Thus, the pressure of 5 tons on $\frac{1}{16}$ of a square inch gives 80 tons per square inch, which is well over the yield stress of most used in chassis and, without doubt, the chassis will bend. Pressure must be recognised and diluted to more maneagable proportions.

All this goes to prove that 'large pressures can be set up with small loads over small areas'. The cure, which is remarkably simple, is to spread the load, that is, to make the area that is taking the load bigger. How is this done? One method is to use a simple softwood wedge. Thousands of pounds can, and occasionally are, spent on recovery vehicles and ancillary equipment, but one of the most important **and** cheapest items is rarely seen. This is simply a wedge made of wood costing, at the most, 20p. Such a wedge inserted between the chain and the chassis, can at the stroke of a hammer, transform a bearing surface of $\frac{1}{16}$ of a square inch to 2 × 4 = 8 in^2 and thus a pressure of 80 tons per square inch on the chassis to five-eights of a ton per square inch. Some difference—and all at the stroke of a hammer.

If there is any doubt in your mind about the efficiacy of a wedge, have a look at it afterwards and see the imprint of the chain. The great thing is, that this wedge, which is so easily used, and does so much work, actually offers a bonus. There is no easier way of tightening a chain, wire or rope than driving two wedges in the way shown in *Figure 20*. Use the wedges longest side down to give an even greater bearing surface.

Figure 20

Now let's go back to our truck, where we were about to subject our chassis to something like 73 tons per square inch. We can start winching and without any doubt at all, over she will come, possibly breaking a spring and certainly doing some damage.

Now, what can we do to prevent any possible damage? Well, maybe you can arrange for a pile of tyres to be placed where the wheels will land, or you can use some low pressure air bags—anything in fact to absorb the shock. Alternatively, you can use a different system altogether to pull it upright.

Let's pretend we have just arrived and start again. This time we are going to try using a righting lever. An excellent piece of equipment for light vehicles with flimsy bodies. Furniture vans, buses, and the like. Not, under any circumstances, to be used with laden vehicles. If this is fitted to the chassis with suitably attached chains, we now have the following situation. We've already decided that the force needed to return the truck to the upright was 16 ton.ft (4 tons × 4 feet from T the fulcrum). We now have a lever 11 ft long working for us. What is the winch pull this time? Again if E is the winch pull then

$$E = \frac{16 \text{ ton.ft}}{11 \text{ ft}} = 1.45 \text{ tons; say } 1\frac{1}{2} \text{ tons.}$$

So far, so good but, referring to *Figure 21*, let us examine the pressure where the chain crosses the chassis under tension, at Z (the chain at Y has only enough tension on it to keep it tight and hold the bar). First of all, work out the force to which the upper chassis member is subjected. We know that we have a force of 1½ tons on the end of the bar, and that the bar is 9 ft long. Now, most chassis are built so that their members are about 2 ft 8 in (2⅔ ft) apart. Consider the moments about Y. If Y is considered as the fulcrum, we have 1½ tons × 9 ft

= 13½ ton.ft working to the right (clockwise), balanced by the load at Z. So if the load at Z is, say Z tons, then

$$Z = \frac{13½ \text{ ton.ft}}{2\frac{2}{3} \text{ ft}} = 5 \text{ tons}$$

and if, as before, the chain around the chassis at Z is adjusted similarly and has a bearing surface of, say, one-eighth of a square inch, then the pressure will be 8 × 5 = 40 tons per square inch. Again, as mild steel will fail at about 30 tons per square inch, a wedge will be necessary. By the way, there are no prizes for guessing where, on the chassis the bar should have been fitted.

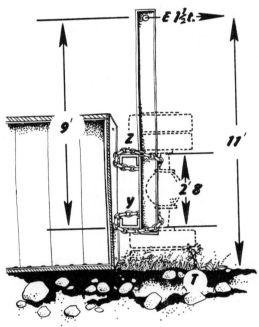

Figure 21

So, having hammered in several wedges we can start winching and again, the casualty will come crashing down. We now have another pro-found moral: 'large pressures can be set up with small forces on long levers over small areas'. There is, however, something else, and a look at *Figure 22* will reveal all. Make full use of your equipment. Use your crane, particularly if you have an extending jib. A powered extending *and* retracting jib is even better.

Now what happens? Well, winch (or if you have a fully powered jib, use it instead of the winch) until we get to the position shown (see *Figure 23*). Then the casualty being, on the point of balance, the weight is taken by the crane and lowered to the ground. Just make sure that when getting close up to the casualty in order to do this evolution, you don't get *too* close. Estimate the arc of the end of the lever and make sure that you keep on the outside of the arc.

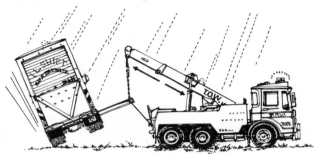

Figure 22

An even better method is as follows. Fully extend your crane boom. Pass the winch cable over a snatch block at the boom head. Retract the boom, which will fetch the casualty to the point of balance, then, *lower* with the winch, retracting the boom at the same time. There is one important point to make here, and that is the change in the lever system at the changeover from righting to lowering. For example, in the first instance, the fulcrum is at Y and all the load taken at Z (trying to pull the chassis away) and pushing Y towards the bodywork, and in the latter instance the fulcrum is at Z and Z is being forced upwards and Y is under tension. So make sure that your chains are nice and tight—all of them—and use plenty of wedges (see *Figure 23*).

At long last we have our casualty back on its feet. We have reached the end of the beginning and can make a beginning of the end.

From all the arithmetic just mentioned it might seem as though a pocket calculator should be an essential part of Recovery Equipment, but the important thing is, to *estimate* the following:

1. The weight of the casualty.
2. The position of the centre of gravity.
3. The distance of the C of G from the tipping point (fulcrum).
4. The distance of the fulcrum from the point of effort.

The rest is knowledge of your equipment.

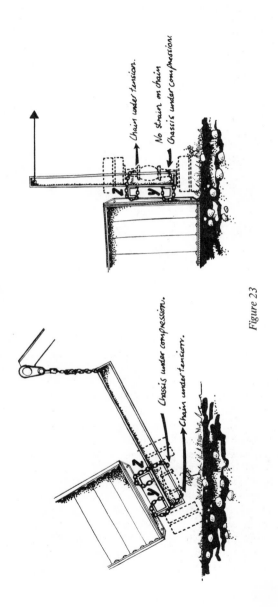

Chain under tension.

No strain on chain.

Chassis under compression.

Chassis under compression.

Chain under tension.

Figure 23

Articulated vehicles

It is one thing righting an unloaded short wheelbase, four wheeler, and quite another in the case of an artic.

The problem is the fifth wheel coupling and the strains imposed upon it if the tractor unit is not supported.

In the first instance the tractor will only move when the coupling pin exerts enough leverage to start it moving, then, still being unsupported, when the point of balance is reached, the tractor will flop over first (because its C of G is lower than that of the trailer) and exert another severe strain upon the pin (*Figure 24*).

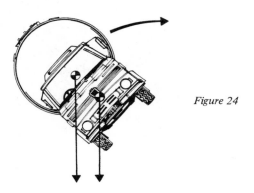

Figure 24

This seems to be the very nub of the problem. Dealing with two centres of gravity, which obviously require two separate calculations and in practice two such problems cannot reasonably be handled simultaneously.

Try to consider the artic as one vehicle with one C of G—as indeed you would in the case of an eight wheeler. In fact, that's exactly what you would have if the fifth wheel coupling plates were clamped together. In practice this is easier than it sounds, because if a strap was chained to the tractor chassis, taken round the trailer, and then chained again to the other side of the tractor chassis and then suitably tightened, that's exactly what you would have accomplished. Of course, there are the problems of pressure which can be resolved by the judicious use of wedges where the chains pass round the chassis members, and by the use of nice, wide, nylon strops elsewhere.

As the whole thing will have to be as rigid as possible, the same wedges will help, but it may be found necessary to use a rigging screw (what do *you* call these things with a left hand thread at one end of a

tube and a right hand thread at the other?). We now have our rigid
artic. Now use whatever method suits you to right it.

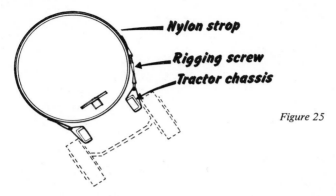

Nylon strop

Rigging screw

Tractor chassis

Figure 25

Just one more thing. Although Isaac Newton can claim credit for
many of the natural laws of dynamics and statics, the most important
single law to operate is *Sods Law*, which states that: 'The inexplicable
perversity of inanimate objects will always prevail'.

Chapter 4

AIR BAGS

Air bags can be used to great effect, and remarkably quickly by those who have troubled to gain experience with them.

How do they work? Its all a matter of spreading the load. You will recall that in a previous chapter it was suggested that heavy loads spread over small areas set up enormous pressures. Well the converse is also true, that large areas with small pressures move heavy loads.

Consider an area of say 1800 in^2 which, roughly speaking is the area of a 4 ft diameter circle, which, is the size of the average Air Bag. If this area is subjected to a pressure of, say, 7 lb/in^2, you will have available a force of 5.6 tons. Acquire three air bags, and you have nearly 17 tons of force ready to do your bidding.

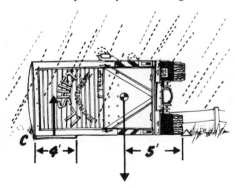

Figure 26

Have a look at our truck again, on its side as usual (see *Figure 26*).

If the truck weighs 6 tons, and the centre of gravity is 5 ft from the fulcrum (the edge of the tyres as before) then we have a Moment of Force of 5 ft × 6 tons = 30 ton.ft to be overcome.

24

Sizing up the operation. The recovery vehicle is manoeuvered into place to give as near as possible a direct pull along the vehicle axis. The rear wheels of the tandem axle are chocked up on wedges

2 *As a safety measure, broad strops girdle the van at a roughly equal distance from each end, with a gun tackle rove to advantage. Air bags are set under the van side as near as possible to the roof, but clear of the damaged panelling (see Figure 27b). Note the pile of sleepers to pivot and support the front end of the semitrailer when righted.*

3 A minor mishap (which could have been a major one). One of the air bags has burst through petrol contamination from an earlier recovery, but the assistance from the crane takes the load

4 The remaining three bags still give sufficient lift and the operation continues. The casualty is righted, with two operators at the winch controls and one keeping a close watch on the air bags

(Photos by courtesy of D. G. McAlister)

Now, if we take a couple of air bags, and place them with due care and attention at C (Question, how far is C from our fulcrum? 12 ft?) So we have to overcome a moment of 30 ton.ft with a lever 12 ft long in order to lift the truck, which is 30 divided by 12 which is 2½ tons of effort. But this is only true if half the bag is used; that is to say, if the bag is only just put under the edge of the roof of the truck. If the whole bag is sited as in *Figure 27(b)* then the lever is shorter; it is not, in fact, 12 ft at all but only 10 ft. Why? well you are not, as in the case of a crane, using a point force, you are in fact using a force spread over a considerable area. The thing to consider here is the centre of effort, this is similar to the centre of gravity (which is, as you know, the point through which the whole weight of an object acts). The Centre of Effort then is the point through which the whole effort can be said to act.

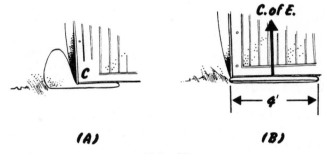

(A)   *(B)*

Figure 27

For example, take this air bag. The force is operating over the end which is 4 ft in diameter. Therefore the Centre of Effort will be at the centre of the bag—in this case, down from the roof of the truck. Thus, our lever is only 10 ft long, and the force required will be 3 tons, not 2½ as above.

Two bags exert a total effort of 3 tons (1½ tons each) or, roughly, 3400 lb each. We are agreed that there are 1800 in^2 in each bag in contact with out truck, so the pressure must be 3400 divided by 1800 equals just under 2 lb/in^2. However this advantage has to be paid for.

Do you remember when we were talking about snatch blocks, mechanical advantage and such like? Then we paid with the velocity ratio. With air bags the penalty is *volume*.

Suppose the air bag is 5 ft high when inflated. We already know that it has an end area of 1800 in^2 which is 12½ ft^2. So, we have a volume of 12½ × 5 = 62½ ft^3. Therefore, we need 62½ ft^3 to fill the bag up to atmospheric pressure (14½ lb/in^2). How much do you need to fill it to 16½ lb/in² (14½ lb/in² plus the 2 lb/in² from our previous calculation)?

Now we have come to Boyle's law which states 'if the temperature of a gas is kept constant, then the volume will be inversely proportional to the pressure.' Very profound, no doubt, but it means that if the pressure is doubled, then the volume is halved, or, in the form of an equation:

$$\frac{\text{Vol a}}{\text{Vol b}} = \frac{\text{Press b}}{\text{Press a}}$$

In our case, the figures look like this:

$$\frac{\text{Vol a}}{62.5} = \frac{16.5}{14.5}$$

$$\text{Vol a} = \frac{62.5 \times 16.5}{14.5} = 71.12 \text{ ft}^3 \text{ in each bag}$$

$\therefore$ 142 ft³ in total

If you had wanted to go up to 7 lb/sq in in each bag, then you would have needed about 93 ft³ of air in each, or 186 ft³ in total, which is an awful lot of air.

The first problem is fitting yourself up with sufficient kit to complete the operation. We need four bags with capacity to fill them, plus of course a bank of valves complete with pressure gauges.

Having done that, the job is very simple, provided that the following precautions are taken:

(a) *Placing the bags.* Avoid the odd projection which can and will (given half the chance) puncture your bag. Take care to avoid the bags 'popping' out when half inflated due to insecure ground, damp bodywork, damp bags.

(b) It has been known for a bag to be split due to the joining solution being disolved by petrol being spilt over it in the course of an operation. So, a secure back-up system is strongly advised, either by continuous chocking, or by using your crane or winch, or both.

(c) Make doubly sure that, when lifting a vehicle, the wheels are securely chocked, otherwise the bags could pop out.

Chapter 5

ROPES, WIRES AND CHAINS

ROPES

Traditionally rope is made from natural fibres such as hemp, sisal, manila and coir; the best and strongest is manila. The white rope is usually sisal. In these days, man-made fibres are more common; these can be of terylene, nylon, etc. Unlike natural fibres, man-made fibres will not rot. However, it is important to remember that heat (particularly heat caused by friction) may destroy synthetics while natural fibres are generally more resistant to heat and compression.

Rope is made up of a number of fibres twisted together to form a strand and a number of strands—usually three, but sometimes four—are laid up, usually right handed, sometimes left handed to form the rope. You can see from this that there are many kinds of rope using different materials, different construction, differing number of parts, and different sizes. For our purposes, however, we are mainly concerned with three-stranded, right-hand lay, and usually made of sisal or possibly manila.

Right-hand lay

Hold a piece of rope in your right hand and point your (right) thumb in the direction that the rope leaves you. If, when you curl your fingers around the rope they coincide with the strands, you are holding Right-hand lay rope.

Rope used to be measured by its circumference but nowadays is measured by diameter in the UK and USA. The *approximate* Breaking Strain, in tons, of a natural fibre rope can be found by applying the formula: $C^2/3$ where C is the circumference. Thus, a 3 in rope (about 1 in diameter) is

$$\frac{3 \times 3}{3} \text{ tons} \; = \; 3 \text{ tons}$$

This is the breaking strain.

The Safe Working Load is $1/5$ th of the Breaking Strain; in this case $3/5$ tons = 12 cwt.

Maintenance of ropes

Keep the rope as dry as possible; if it gets wet, as it probably will, it may rot, so hang it up in a dry, warm place. Examine the rope from time to time by opening up the lay and inspecting the innards for dampness or mildew. Coil right-hand lay rope in a clockwise direction. To avoid fraying, whip or splice the ends. Natural fibre ropes can be preserved using Stockholm tar. Many ropes are so treated before processing.

WIRE ROPE

Wire rope, like fibre rope, is a most complicated subject. We will confine ourselves to six-stranded wire rope with fibre core, with right-hand lay (same rule as last time). Even so, there are many different kinds. For example, in steel wire ropes there are at least three kinds of steel used—80/90 ton; 90/100 ton; 100/110 ton tensile. For the sake of safety, unless you *know* different, and assume you have the 80/90 ton wire rope.

As with fibre rope, a wire rope is made up of a number of wires twisted together and, in this case, six strands laid up from these around a fibre core. Some wire rope is laid up the same way as the original wires were twisted, called Langs lay, but we will confine ourselves to

Wires twisted into spiral

Figure 28

ordinary lay, where the strands are laid up in the opposite direction to the way the original wires were twisted. Note that the term 'twisted' is used loosely. Indeed most wire rope these days is 'preformed'; that is, you get a number of wires formed into a spiral (*Figure 28*).

Now, as to construction, and this is the crux of the matter. Start with a number of preformed wires—say 19 in this case—and lay them up to form a strand (see *Figure 29*). Take six strands and lay them up over a fibre core. What we have now is a preformed wire rope of the

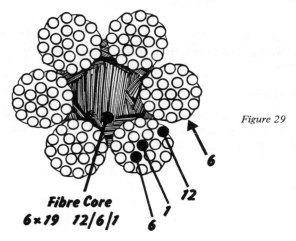

Figure 29

Fibre Core
6 × 19   12/6/1

6 × 19 group over a fibre core. Now this is a main group, and, of course, there are several different kinds of construction within this group and the differences are the way the wires are laid up in each strand. Take 6 × 19 (12/6/1) for example. As before, the 6 is the number of strands, whilst the 12/6/1 bit means that 12 wires form an outer ring, over six wires in the secondary ring, over a single wire centre (note that 12 + 6 + 1 = 19) so, 6 × 19 group. Alternatively, you could get, still within the 6 × 19 group, 6 × 19 (9/9/1).

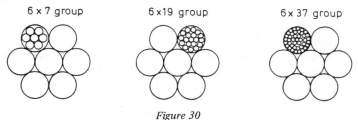

6 x 7 group   6 x 19 group   6 x 37 group

Figure 30

The whole idea of using wire rope is that we require the strength of steel and the flexibility of fibre. Flexibility depends upon the number of wires used in the construction. With only one wire, you would have a high tensile steel bar and no flexibility. If, on the other hand you wanted a very high degree of flexibility you could choose a wire rope of the 6 × 37 group (37 wires). Naturally, if we want a 1 in diameter rope, the one with 37 strands will have very thin wires; if you had chosen from the 6 × 7 group you would have thick wires, but just try to coil it!

Figure 30 shows a diagram of the three groups.

In general, therefore, the 6 × 19 group is chosen for winch cables, which is a good compromise between the rigidity and toughness of the 6 × 7 and the flexibility of the 6 × 37 group.

As to the core, this is usually jute impregnated with oil. When the rope is under tension, the core is squeezed, and this releases the oil and thus lubricates each and every wire. Talking of lubrication, very few people have even seen a lubricated winch rope; most are covered in mud and rust. Problems arise with lubrication due to the fact that two criteria have to be met and for two purposes:

1. (a)   The oil has to be thin to penetrate all the wires, and
   (b)   The oil has to have a degree of 'stickability' so that rain or wear and tear will not remove it.

2. (a)   Oil has to lubricate each wire so that it can 'roll over' its neighbour, and
   (b)   Has to protect each wire from rust.

Fish oil seems to meet all of these needs.

As to inspection and maintenance, it is a good idea once every three months to wind the cable out to its extreme limit and go along it inch by inch looking for three things:

1. *Disturbed lay.* This can be rectified by the judicious use of a marline spike under each disturbed strand and working it along the rope for several feet until it has regained its rightful place. The process can be assisted by tapping gently with a hardwood mallet.

2. *Broken wires.* Broken wires are all too easily found by rubbing your bare hand along the full length of the wire! A certain number of broken wires are permissible before condemning the rope and the rule is: '5% of the wires in 10 diameters'. This sounds very cryptic, but merely means that if you have a 1 in diameter wire, and it's 6 × 19 construction = 114 wires, then you are allowed 5% of 114 = 5.7, say 6 broken wires in any 10 inches of the rope. This number of broken wire will condemn the rope; a fewer number will mean a substantial reduction in its safe working load.

3. *Rust.* This can be removed with a wire brush. Brush the whole wire in the direction of the lay, removing the rust and mud. This will also reveal any broken strands. The worst part of the job is to get two wads of cotton waste, dipping them into the bucket of fish oil, wringing out lightly and applying both hands, still grasping the wads, to the wire and moving along, simultaneously rotating hands to follow the lay. Do not start this job before a night out!

We now come to the question of strength. How strong is it? A rough and ready formula for calculating the Breaking Strain of wire rope is $3C^2$ where C is the circumference of the wire. For example; 1 in diameter wire is approximately 3 in circumference. Therefore the breaking strain = $3 \times 3^2 = 3 \times 3 \times 3 = 27$ tons. The safe working load (SWL) is $\frac{1}{5}$ of the Breaking Strain. So our 1 in wire, with a B.S. of 27 tons has a SWL of $\frac{27}{5} = 5\frac{2}{5}$ tons.

Again, note that this is an approximate method; the table in Appendix 3 is for rope constructed of 100/110 ton tensile material.

CHAIN

It will come as no surprise to learn that there are several kinds of chain but for our use we are only concerned with the grade of steel from which the chain is formed. So we have:

Grade 40   —   cheapest and heaviest
Grade 60   —   higher tensile
Grade 75   —   very special
Grade T   —   even more special

You may perhaps have noticed that the higher the grade number, the better the quality the steel and thus a thinner chain for a given strength. In fact the breaking strain of any chain (in tons) can be calculated by multiplying the grade Number (GNo) by the square of the diameter of the bar from which it was made (B.S. = GNo $\times d^2$).

For example, take a ½ in chain of grade 75 material, the Breaking Strain will be $75 \times \frac{1}{2} \times \frac{1}{2} = 18.75$ tons, and the SWL is $\frac{1}{5}$ of the Breaking Strain. Just to compare, a ½ in chain of grade 40 will be $40 \times \frac{1}{2} \times \frac{1}{2} = 10$ tons Breaking Strain (2 tons SWL). The grade number of a British chain, by the way, is stamped on a link at three foot intervals.

Any doubt about grade T chain can be quelled by saying 'for T—read 80'.

A small problem exists over grab links—those with a diamond section. Due to the fact that they can be fitted in the centre of a link and that they have a very small bearing area and that acting at right angles to

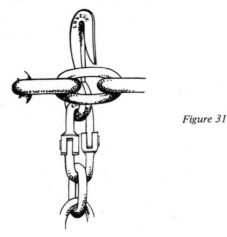

Figure 31

the direction of the main chain (*Figure 31*), the SWL has been reduced by 50%. The best system is the positive chain clutch, because the bearing area is greater and it pulls parallel to the main chain direction.

Inspection and maintenance

Every link must be examined separately for three things:

1. *Cracks.*
2. *Link elongation.* Instead of the link being slightly egg shaped, the two long sides will be parallel and if severe, the adjoining links will be locked (or nearly so) and,
3. *Bearing wear.* The bar diameter will be reduced, by pure wear.

Conditions 2 and 3 will result in that interesting (and dangerous) phenomenon of a chain that is as stiff and unyielding as a bar of iron. All these conditions can be avoided by proper use, within the SWL of the chain and with proper inspection and maintenance.

Maintenance is simple—just dip the chain into a bucket of oil—preferably *after* inspection. Alternatively, the chain can be painted with a very good wire treatment compound which dries well and protects both wire and chain from rust.

Chapter 6

TACKLES

Tackles are used for two reasons:

1. To change direction of effort, and
2. To gain Mechanical Advantage.

The arrangement shown in *Figure 32* is used to change the direction of effort and there is no Mechanical Advantage. In fact the friction of the pulley will have to be overcome, which will be less if the oil can has

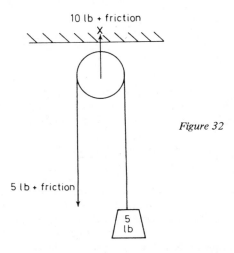

10 lb + friction

5 lb + friction

5 lb

Figure 32

been used. Note that the force on the holdfast X will be the weight of the load, plus the effort, i.e. 5 lb + 5 lb + friction = 10 + lb. In *Figure 33* we have the same hardware used to create a Mechanical Advantage. Note that here the weight on the holdfast is the effort

33

(which includes friction) only, whilst the force on the snatch block hook is the load.

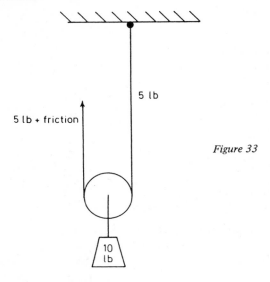

5 lb

5 lb + friction

Figure 33

10 lb

Thus, the Mechanical Advantage is 2:1.

Rule: Mechanical Advantage $= \dfrac{Load}{Effort}$

As everyone knows, you get nothing without paying for it. The price of lifting a 10 lb load with only 5 lb plus of effort, is that you have to exert the effort for twice the distance. This is known as *Velocity Ratio:*

Velocity Ratio $= \dfrac{\text{Distance moved by load}}{\text{Distance moved by effort}}$

In our case, then, for every foot moved by the load, you have to pull the rope two feet. A lot of rope is needed for the more complicated layups. Look at a few examples. In *Figure 34* the mechanical advantage is 2:1. Thus, the Recovery Vehicle is only required to exert half the force required to move the casualty. The other half is taken by the holdfast. The Velocity Ratio is 1:2, thus, if the casualty has to be moved 50 ft, the 100 ft cable will have to be winched.

The arrangement shown in *Figure 35* is more complicated using two snatch blocks and a holdfast. Mechanical Advantage is 3:1 and Velocity

Ratio 1:3. $\frac{1}{3}$W is taken by the Recovery Vehicle, $\frac{2}{3}$W taken by the Holdfast.

Note the following:

1. *Friction* Allow about 10% of the winch pull for each snatch block used; this is the usual rough Recovery Vehicle type block. If the block is *well* maintained allow 5%.
2. Note the weights taken by both the holdfast and the Recovery Vehicle.

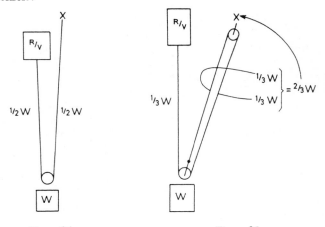

Figure 34   Figure 35

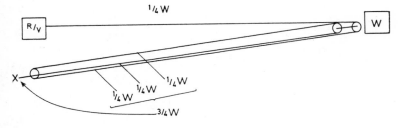

Figure 36

Figure 36 shows another layup using three snatch blocks, or two if you have a double sheave block. Mechanical Advantage is 4:1 and the Velocity Ratio 1:4. There is only ¼ W on the recovery vehicle but ¾ W on holdfast. It needs to be a good lift. There is a fair amount of friction here too.

Another way to approach the same problem which reduces the number of snatch blocks (and therefore friction) and also distributes the load more evenly is shown in *Figure 37*. This is where an extra length of wire rope can come in very handy.

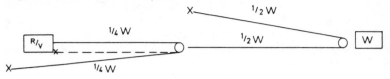

Figure 37

A final word on mechanical advantage. In practice, to find the MA count the number of (rope) parts at the moving block. Two distinctly different ways of using the same hardware are illustrated in *Figure 39*.

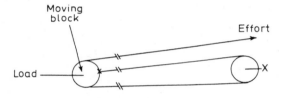

Figure 38

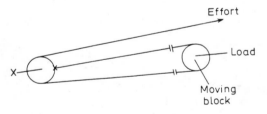

Figure 39

The arrangement in *Figure 38*, in nautical parlance, is a 'Gun Tackle'. This is 'rove to advantage' a nice term which means that you have the best possible out of your kit. The mechanical advantage (MA) is 3:1; (note the three parts at the moving block) and that the direction of effort is the same as that of the load movement. Now, look at *Figure 39*. Still the same hardware, still a Gun Tackle, but 'rove to disadvantage'.

Obvious, but you only have a MA of 2:1 (count the number of parts at the moving block). Note that the direction of effort is opposite to the load movement.

Chapter 7

SNATCH BLOCKS

A snatch block can either be single or double sheave, with a 'gate' to admit the rope, thus precluding the necessity of threading it through.

A 'gin' block, on the other hand, is usually a single sheave block and without the 'gate'. Most people would prefer to let someone else use a gin block in recovery work. There is an area of doubt and some mystification about blocks. What does it mean to have a 5 ton block? It means, in fact, that you can exert a 5 ton line pull on the rope within the block (see *Figure 40*). However, if one is lifting a 5 ton load with a rope rove through a block, the said block is subjected to a direct load of the 5 tons of weight plus the 5 tons of effort, i.e. 10 tons.

Therein lies the reason why most people complain at the size of snatch block they are forced to carry around with them. The common plea is 'why can't I have a nice small block like so and so has?' Well, now you know. There is another reason for large snatch blocks and a glance at the chapter on wire ropes again will serve to remind the reader that although wire rope is made to bend, if it is bent through too small a radius it will stretch or break the individual wires.

As a general rule, the diameter of the sheave of any block should be approximately 16 times the diameter of the wire. Thus, ideally, a 1 in wire should have a 16 in snatch block. A 12 in block is just about OK, but *not* a 6 in block. Naturally snatch blocks (even single ones) are very heavy. They have to be for all the reasons given above. For example, if you are the person driving the winch, and should the becket or the eye of your block fail, there is no doubt that you are in its line of flight and even if you take a similar line of flight, you will be overtaken. The moral is that it is better to buy a big block.

Together with most other pieces of recovery equipment, the snatch block suffers from the popular misconception that it thrives on hard work and ill treatment and if it is oiled or greased it will become soft and unreliable.

Only professionals seem to bother with such niceties—seamen, fishermen, miners, and the like maintain their equipment with almost fanatical care. Maybe it is time that we joined their ranks.

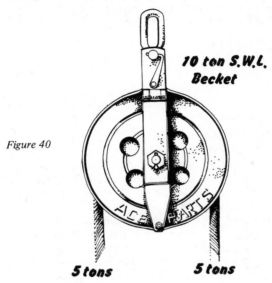

Figure 40

Finally, here is a rough table of snatch block sizes, the size of rope they are made for, their main dimensions and weight. Use this table the next time you buy a snatch block.

Sheave Dia.	To Suit Rope Dia.	S.W.L. (Becket)	S.W.L.(Wire) 110 Ton Tensile
6 in	$7/16$ —½ in	3 tons	1¾ tons
8 in	¾ in	6 tons	4 tons
10 in	¾ in	8 tons	4 tons
12 in	$7/8$ in	10 tons	5 tons
14 in	$15/16$ in	10 tons	6¼ tons
16 in	$1 3/8$ in	20 tons	14 tons

Chapter 8

ROUGH IDEAS ON ROUGH TERRAIN

To move any vehicle from rest, three forces have to be overcome:
1. Rolling resistance.
2. Grade resistance.
3. Air resistance.

Being practical people who cannot winch a vehicle at 50 miles an hour, we can forget about the air resistance and concentrate on the other two.

For all practical purposes Rolling Resistance results from the friction of moving parts, the capacity for tyres to stick to the road, or, in the case of a vehicle off the road, mud suction, sinkage, etc.

Naturally enough, the Rolling Resistance differs according to the kind of terrain you are in at the time. For example, the force required to move a vehicle on a flat, tarmac road is approximately $\frac{1}{25}$ th of the weight of the vehicle, in other words, it takes about a ton of effort to move a twenty five ton truck which is stopped on a flat road.

To clarify the matter, imagine putting a large set of spring scales between your winch cable and the point of connection to the casualty; you would get a reading of about a ton on the dial. Note the word 'about'—these are not hard and fast rules, but just approximations based upon experience.

So far, experiment has shown that the following are the 'best' approximations for various kinds of terrain:

Type of Surface	Pulling power				
Road	$\frac{1}{25}$ th	of weight of casualty			
Grass	$\frac{1}{7}$ th	,,	,,	,,	,,
Gravel	$\frac{1}{5}$ th	,,	,,	,,	,,
Soft sand	$\frac{1}{4}$ th	,,	,,	,,	,,
Shallow mud	$\frac{1}{3}$ rd	,,	,,	,,	,,
Bog	$\frac{1}{2}$	,,	,,	,,	,,

Remember that, so far, all the surfaces are supposed to be flat. Grade Resistance comes next and, of course, will have to be added to the figures from the table. For Grade Resistance there is one simple rule, (again approximate), which is this:

'The force to overcome Grade Resistance for a vehicle is roughly $\frac{1}{60}$th of the weight of the vehicle for every $1°$ of slope, up to an angle of $45°$ where the whole weight of the casualty can be considered'.

So, if you have a thirty ton casualty to pull up a $30°$ slope, which is in effect a grassy slope, two separate calculations have to be made:

Rolling Resistance—grass—$\frac{1}{7}$th of the weight (from the table) is $\frac{1}{7}$th of 30 tons is $4\frac{2}{7}$ tons.

Grade Resistance—$30°$ $30 \text{ tons} \times \dfrac{1}{60} \times 30° = \dfrac{900}{60} = 15 \text{ tons}$

The Total Resistance is therefore $15 + 4\frac{2}{7}$ or $19\frac{2}{7}$ tons, say $19\frac{1}{2}$ tons.

WINCHES

Now, armed with these figures, let's look at winches and explode a few popular myths. One myth compels a lot of people to insist that they have a 40 ton winch aboard their Diamond 'T' and the like; even when the manufacturers insist that it has a ten ton capacity. Another myth compels people to say that they had 60 tons on the end of their winch cable, when it would have broken long ago.

A winch is merely a machine for creating a mechanical advantage. In a winch, this is done by two methods:

1. By gearing, usually worm and wheel, and
2. By leverage by adjusting the size of the drum.

Going back to the power source—the main engine. Suppose, for the sake of argument that the engine has a power output of 450 lb.ft of torque (remember the bit about moments of force?). This torque is transmitted through the gearbox, which in low gear has a gearing of, say, 5.5:1—mechanical advantage (with the corresponding velocity ratio). Now, if the output shaft is connected directly to the input shaft of the winch, we have available 2000 lb.ft of torque (knock off a couple of hundred for frictional losses leaving 1800 lb.ft).

Most heavy winches, including the Gar Wood and Scammel units, have worm and wheel drive. For the sake of the exercise let's assume a 30:1 reduction at the worm and wheel, thus giving 1800 × 30 lb.ft at the periphery of the wheel. In the case of the Gar Wood unit, this is the same diameter as the drum; so, at the drum we have 54000 lb of direct line pull if we ignore the heavy frictional losses within the worm and wheel train (maybe 30%) which is considerably less than the 40 tons mentioned in the first place.

In fact, the Gar Wood winch on a Series 980/981; 6 × 4 Diamond 'T' has a torque cut out of 22.400 lb line pull.

Naturally, a winch will have a smaller capacity when a greater number of layers of rope are on the drum. This is because it effectively increased the size of the drum and thus naturally has the effect of gearing up the winch, thus losing capacity.

A compromise has to be reached concerning winch drums; on one hand we require a small drum for greater leverage but a large drum to conform with our ideas on wire ropes being wrapped around too small circumferences. In the case of a Diamond T or a Scammell, an average of a 1 in diameter rope is used giving an average SWL of 7 tons.

Perhaps we can now buy the idea of a 40 ton winch being fitted to a truck.

Chapter 9

WINCHING

The winch is one of the most powerful pieces of equipment on a recovery vehicle, and can cause a lot of damage when improperly used. When used in conjunction with a system as described in the previous chapter it is a most effective tool, but requires a lot of thought both before and during use.

Perhaps the most important point to make is the distribution of the forces involved. For example, an 8-ton recovery vehicle cannot and will not move a 30-ton casualty (no matter how many snatch blocks are used) if all the load is taken on the recovery vehicle. In short, estimate the load to be winched, know your own winch capacity, look at the terrain, and calculate your layout.

For example, suppose that we have a 30-ton gross casualty on a 15° grassed slope. The weight of the Recovery Vehicle is 12 tons. The winch capacity is 10 tons. Let's do it step by step.

Step 1. Grass: So rolling resistance will be about $^{30}/_7 = 4^2/_7$ tons, say 4½ tons.

Step 2. Slope is 15° (Question: is this the average slope of the maximum that will be encountered?) Have another look along the proposed winching track and perhaps push up the estimate to 20°, so $^{30}/_{60} \times 20 = 10$ tons.

First Part of Answer. The required winch pull will be 14½ tons approx, say, 15 tons. At this point it may be as well to remember that a boulder, lump of earth, or such like, sited directly under a wheel, may constitute what may amount to a 45° slope (consult table in previous chapter). In this case our 15 tons increases to 35 tons.

43

Step 3. Having 10 tons winch capacity and 15 tons to exert, indicates a 2:1 layup, that is, one snatch block attached to the casualty. One snatch block means about 10% friction, so add 1½ tons, giving a total of 16½ tons and, yes, its still within the capacity of a 2 to 1 system.

Step 4. Question: what size snatch block is needed? 8½ tons is OK if you've got one, but you are more likely to have a 10 tonner. Let's use that one. But we're still adrift. The recovery vehicle only weighs 15 tons, has no spades. and of course will winch itself backwards, which will raise a few eyebrows if not the roof. So what now? Look around for a tree (don't be tempted to use the telegraph pole) use your ground anchors or stop an eight wheeler. Most haulage companies would prefer you to be equipped with ground anchors; only in their own Recovery Vehicles are they not needed.

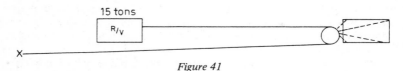

Figure 41

Now we have the set up as in *Figure 41*, which seems to be OK. But how is the snatch block attached to the casualty? The total force being applied is 16½ tons. Only one chain on, say, the front axle, might bend the latter or, perhaps pull it free from the spring hangers. It might be a good idea to put a bridle on the axle together with another attached to another axle. This means that the 16½ tons is spread to four points of contact and, if wedges are used, all should be in order. Naturally, it's

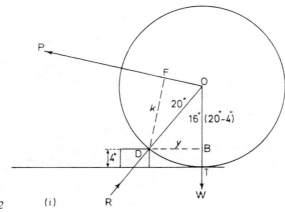

Figure 42   (i)

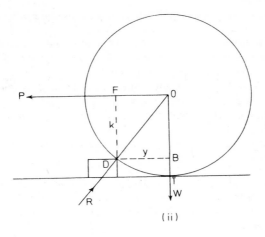

(ii)

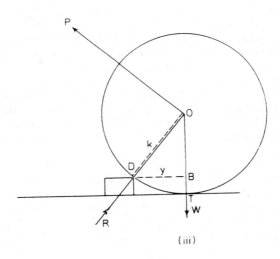

(iii)

Figure 42 (continued)

important when using double bridles to get the same tension on each leg otherwise you have wasted your time. In most cases, the judicious use of wedges can adjust tension to quite a fine degree.

The point of maximum loading is now where the snatch block is joined to the two bridles and seems to indicate an 18 ton shackle.

Step 5. Make a final check and ask yourself these questions:

1. As the truck is loaded; will the load stand being winched or will the high centre of gravity cause it to tip over if one wheel sinks into the inevitable soft patch?
2. What will happen if the winch wire breaks? Which direction will the free ends of the wire go?
3. In what direction will the snatch block move if that shackle breaks?
4. How can I protect my winch cable and snatch block when coming over the brow? (if there is a brow)

Question 4 can easily be answered. The cable and block can be protected by using a *snatch block toboggan.* This is usually made from $\frac{1}{8}$ in mild steel plate and allows the block to slide over the ground rather than cut through it.

An additional factor to be reckoned with when calculating a required winch line pull, is the unexpected but usual bug of having a stone, rock, or other impediment under one or more (usually more) wheels.

Just as an example, let us calculate how much winching effort is required to pull a truck over, say, a housebrick, which has inadvertantly been placed just under one wheel, say a front wheel.

Some information is necessary—what is the weight of the wheel? What is the size of the wheel? What is the size of the impediment—the brick? Let's imagine that we have a fully loaded truck on 10.00 × 20 tyres, with an axle loading of 6 tons. The brick is 4 in high.

Look at the sketch in *Figure 42(i).* Three forces are acting on the wheel.

1. The line pull required on the winch—represented by P in the direction OP. This is the one we want.
2. The weight of the wheel on the ground—represented by W in the direction of OW. This is half the axle load and is thus 3 tons.
3. The resistance of the brick to the wheel—represented by R in the direction of RO.

We do not know the force at R, so if we take moments about its line of force at a convenient place, we can ignore it. So let's take moments about D, the point of impact of the brick with the wheel. *Figure 43(ii)* shows the levers DB and DF at right angles to the other forces involved.

The wheel will begin to move when the moment P × k overcomes the moment W × y.

More formally: when

$$P \times k = W \times y$$

Now,

$$k = OB \text{ and } OB = OT - BT$$

OT is half the wheel diameter, and so is OD which is 20 in (10.00 ×
20 tyres).

$$BT \text{ is the height of the brick } = 4 \text{ in.}$$

Therefore

$$OB = 20 - 4 = 16$$

Thus, the formal $P \times k = W \times y$ becomes:

$$P \text{ tons} \times 16 \text{ in} = 3 \text{ tons} \times y \text{ in}$$

However, according to Pythagoras

$$y = \sqrt{(OD^2 - OB^2)}$$

so

$$y = \sqrt{(20^2 - 16^2)} = \sqrt{144} = 12 \text{ in}$$

so

$$P \text{ tons} \times 16 \text{ in} = 3 \text{ tons} \times 12 \text{ in}$$

$$P = \frac{3 \text{ tons} \times 12 \text{ in}}{16 \text{ in}} = 2\tfrac{1}{4} \text{ tons}$$

Findings? Well add this force to your previous calculations, or,
better still, make with the spade.

Of course, with a bit of thought, even this force can be minimised,
that is, if the brick cannot be moved.

Consider *Figure 42(iii)*. The greatest value of k, and thus the smallest
value of P will be when the direction of P is at right angles to the line
OD. The lever k is now exactly the same length as OD, i.e. 20 in.

Going back to the formula: P will now equal

$$\frac{3 \times 12}{20} = 1.80 \text{ tons.}$$

This is a reduction of 20% from the original findings, and is all due
to a bit of thought.

NOTES AND SUGGESTIONS

1. Wherever possible when winching, position the recovery vehicle so that you are winching in direct line with the chassis.
2. Avoid forward winching with a centrally mounted winch as it tends to wreck your chassis.
3. Always unwind the winch cable under tension, otherwise a loose coil could become trapped when powering in—with surprising results.
4. When using multiple layups, try and arrange that the winch cable is rove through the sheaves in the same direction; it avoids kinking.

Chapter 10

TOWING

By the very nature of the job, towing is unavoidable. In many ways it is the part of the job that constitutes the greatest danger to the general public and the one that seems to receive the least possible attention—particularly to detail.

We still see people towing on the end of chains and ropes, and even worse, using a Land Rover to tow a loaded commercial vehicle, often by using a rope or chain.

Surprisingly, rigid bars, both swan-necked and straight, seem to be an even greater potential danger due to the fact that most people seem to realise that a rope or chain is 'dodgy' anyway and drive accordingly. Quite often, however, bars are used as if they are endowed with magic qualities and that ordinary common sense can be dispensed with, together with normal precautions.

In the first place, the success or failure of the towing operation depends upon the person steering the casualty. He may never have done it before. In the second place there is the matter of braking. Many tales are told of the driver who was steering the casualty with the engine running to provide air, panics, uses the footbrake and is left languishing in the middle of the road with his front axle being towed away by a 90 ton Prime Mover, the driver of which is quite unaware of the commotion going on astern.

BRAKING

Figure 43 shows a Recovery Vehicle weighing 10 tons and having a braking efficiency of 50% (has yours?). It has the load well distributed.

Figure 44 shows the same vehicle with a paying customer hooked on, going, as it happens downhill. As usual, we have been so anxious to collect his money that we have not had the time to snap the 'suzies' on to provide air to the casualty. Naturally, as the train is going downhill, the centre of gravity of each truck acting vertically downwards, transfers more weight on to the front axle of each vehicle, at the same time

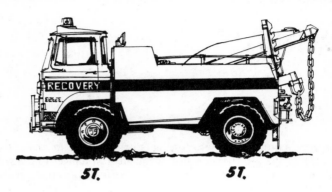

Figure 43

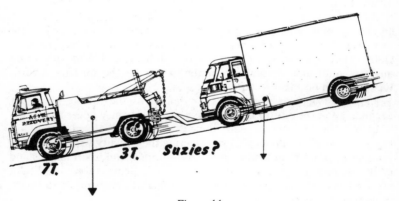

Figure 44

unloading the rear axles. The casualty, acting on the straight line between the points of contact of the swan-necked bar, tends to lift the rear axle of the Recovery Vehicle off the ground; further exacerbating an already undesirable condition. The front axle is already overloaded to the tune of 50% and the rear axle has hardly enough weight on it to provide any kind of stopping power. The recovery vehicle has only to touch his brakes and the front axle will be loaded up even more.

Have a look at the situation from above when the 'train' is faced with a bend, *Figure 45*. It will not take much imagination to work out

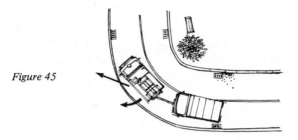

Figure 45

what will happen in the two seconds following a dab on the brakes, so let's do a bit of revision on the basic theory of braking, friction and the like.

FRICTION

If there is no friction, there is no stopping.

Consider the case of a wooden block, on a flat surface. The Coefficient of Friction between the two surfaces is 0.5 (a block of ice on an ice surface could be 0.01 whilst a block of rough concrete on a surface of sandpaper could be 0.9). In our imperfect world it is impossible to get either 0 (indicating no friction) or 1 (indicating complete immovability). Suppose our wooden block weighs 5 lb (*Figure 46*). Then the

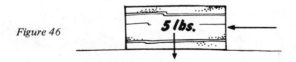

Figure 46

5 lbs.

resistance to movement (back to rolling resistance again) is W times the Coefficient of Friction, which in this case is 5 lb × 0.5 = 2.5 lbf.

Now consider the other side of the story. Let's take a moving vehicle when the brakes are applied. There is now a considerable amount of friction being generated, thus giving a stopping force. To keep it very simple, let us consider that a 50% braking efficiency exerts a braking force of 50% of the weight of the vehicle. A 30 ton truck, then will have 15 tons of braking force available.

Getting back to our original Recovery Vehicle, if on the way out the driver slams on the brakes, there is 5 tons of stopping power or thereabouts acting on two axles, and the vehicle stops quite quickly. On the way back, and just starting down that hill, two things have altered:

1. The gross train weight has gone up to 30 tons.
2. His 50% braking efficiency is knocked sideways because it is only acting mainly on one axle.

Now assume that we have only lost 10% efficiency; we have now 40% efficiency and most people would think this to be a dangerously optimistic estimate.

So we have 40% of 10 tons = 4 tons of retarding force to stop 30 tons which works out to be around 13%. What steps do you take? Well, for a start you could put air where some rubber is. Put on the 'suzies' and connect up to the rear axle output on the treadle valve of the casualty. This would give braking on three axles and you might get a 20% braking efficiency on the 'train'. This gives 20% of 30 tons = 6 tons, which is much better. *Figure 4.7* indicates a better way and has the advantage that the casualty's driver is in your passenger seat.

Another advantage can be seen from the figures. The recovery vehicle has a more manageable front axle and has some traction on the rear axle. Having learnt the lesson, air has been piped back to the casualty (note the wiggly line in the diagram *Figure 47*). Now, we have a 'train' braking efficiency of perhaps 40% i.e. 40% of 12 tons of retarding force.

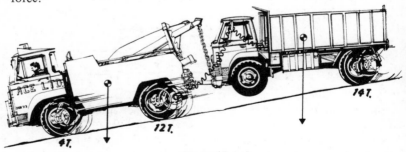

Figure 47

Naturally, in real life, the case is not quite so clear cut as we have differing brake drum areas, pressure drops, etc. However, these facts make the lift and tow much more desirable. Finally, in the example, the recovery vehicle was a four wheeler and weighed 10 tons. This could well have been a 30 ton artic unit converted, and happily, more by luck than judgement, we were working within the designed limits of the braking system with only a 20 tonner being towed. You could just as well have been faced with a 30 ton eight wheeler behind giving a Gross Train Weight of 40 tons. The moral is: 'Don't start what you can't stop'.

It is easy to talk about fitting air lines to the casualty but putting this into practice is a little more difficult. There are certain precautions to take and a handful of differing BSP male/male straight and male 90° male fittings could come in very handy on a cold night. It is well worth the time to make up a few adaptors to fit a range of popular vehicles, so that you have at least a head start.

Some people are keen to take the easy way out and stick a suzie on to an air tank drain cock. If the casualty has been standing about for an hour or two it is dead cold and, if warm air is now introduced into the system, inevitably there will be a certain amount of condensation which will be pumped around. Subsequently, this could cause considerable corrosion. The use of the brain prior to playing about with complicated air systems is of vital importance.

A sticky problem. This articulated tanker carrying glue overturned on a roundabout, twisting the tractor's chassis through nearly 90 degrees and leaving the cab almost upright. The driver insisted on air bags being used in the operation, so the semi-trailer was righted using three bags and two nylon strops winched from the recovery vehicle.

Wooden sleepers bear against heavy metal spikes driven into the road and act as a fulcrum for the casualty's wheels preventing sliding toward the recovery vehicle.

Successfully righted the only damage to the tank was that sustained on impact with the kerb. (Photos by courtesy of D. G. McAlister)

Chapter 11

RECOVERY VEHICLES

In the medium and heavy end of the range, we are concerned with two types:

1. The Light Locomotive which to be classified as such must exceed 7¼ tons kerb weight.
2. Heavy locomotive which must be at least 11½ tons to be so classified.

The legal effects of the above classification will be explained later.

CHOOSING THE RECOVERY VEHICLE

The choice of the correct type of vehicle rests, of course, with the type of work that it will be required to do. It may be that in the future the Law may require a recovery vehicle to comply in all respects to the various laws governing commercial vehicles. It follows, therefore, that we may see the end of tiny and inadequate trucks towing, even at 5 miles an hour, a much larger vehicle—rather like a roller skate pulling an elephant.

Supposing, for the sake of argument, that we have a Heavy Recovery Vehicle. This will be a heavy locomotive weighing in excess of 11½ tons—possibly as much as 14 tons. If this vehicle goes out to recover a 30 ton casualty, the Gross Train Weight will be 41½ tons minimum.

This would appear to indicate that we need as a basic unit a 44/45 ton Prime Mover as a minimum requirement. The power unit and the gearbox will be very suitable for the job but the weak point, inevitably, will be the rear axle. It will have a heavy traction two spring bogie with a capacity of 20 tons, that is 10 tons on each axle. Now suppose the kerb weight of the truck, being 14 tons, is split up as follows:

Front axle — 4 tons
Rear axle (bogie) — 10 tons

This is shown in *Figure 48*.

Figure 48

Question: What weight can be lifted by the crane at a point 6 ft behind the centre of the rear bogie if the wheelbase is 14 ft?

Being purely a question of moments, let's get to work. Consider the truck as a system of levers. Let the bogie centre be called A. First let's find out where the centre of gravity of the vehicle is in respect to the bogie centre.

Taking moments about A (see *Figure 49*).

Then: $W \times G = 4 \text{ tons} \times 14 \text{ ft}$

$14 \text{ tons} \times G = 4 \text{ tons} \times 14 \text{ ft}$

$$G = \frac{4 \times 14}{14} = 4 \text{ feet}$$

So we have the total weight of the truck acting at a point 4 ft in front of the bogie centre.

Back to the lever again:

$$W \times G = T \times 6 \text{ ft}$$

$$14 \text{ tons} \times 4 \text{ ft} = T \times 6 \text{ ft}$$

$$\frac{4 \times 14}{6} = T = 9.33 \text{ tons}$$

Note that the identical figure could have been reached without going to the trouble of finding out where the C of G is, but we need it later on anyway. If, for example, the moment you used was that given by the front axle weight multiplied by the wheel base, exactly the same result would have followed.

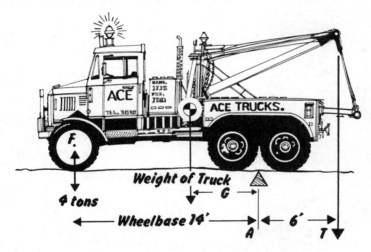

Figure 49

However, to get back. At 9.33 tons, there is a balance, an exact balance. In fact, this is the point at which the front axle will have no weight on it at all, and therefore no steering.

In order to provide sufficient steerage only 60% of the 9.33 tons can be used. The SWL of the vehicle for lift and tow purposes is the 60% of 9.33 tons = 5.60 tons. To do the job properly, let's find out what weight will be imposed upon the bogie when a suspended tow of 5.60 tons is made.

Again, take all the moments about F, the front axle.

We have   W × (Wheelbase − Dist G)

$$= 14 \text{ ft} \times (14 \text{ tons} - 4 \text{ ft})$$

$$= 14 \text{ tons} \times 10 \text{ ft} = 140 \text{ tons.ft.}$$

and, the weight T   = (5.60 tons) × its distance from F

$$= (14 \text{ ft} + 6 \text{ ft} = 20 \text{ ft})$$

The moment   = 5.60 tons × 20

$$= 112 \text{ tons.ft.}$$

Add these together and you get 252 tons.ft, this being the total of moments about F.

Thus, to balance these moments, a force of x tons must react against the bogie centre at A which is 12 ft from F.

Thus, $x = \dfrac{252 \text{ ton.ft}}{14 \text{ ft}} = 18 \text{ tons}$

which is the imposed load on the bogie when the vehicle is operating at its maximum SWL.

Pursue the problem just a little further. What is the weight imposed upon the steering axle? Well, the vehicle is supporting 14 tons—its own

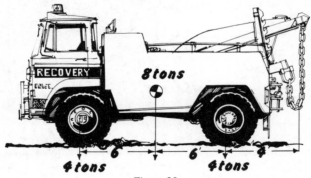

Figure 50

weight, plus 5.60 tons. The imposed weight on the crane. Total 19.60 tons. But 18 tons of this is taken by the bogie, so the rest, 1.60 tons must be taken by the remaining axle.

Consider the ins and outs of these figures whilst we look at a two axle recovery vehicle. This weighs about 8 tons which brings it into the

Light Locomotive classification. The kerb weight could well be distributed thus: 4 tons front axle, 4 tons rear axle. Wheel base approx 12 ft (*Figure 50*).

As we have equal axle loadings, the centre of gravity will be situated exactly between the two axles. So we have 8 tons acting vertically 6 ft in front of the rear axle, ie 48 ton.ft. Divide this by the overhang figure of 4 ft, and we have the maximum weight that can be lifted, ie $^{48}/_4$ = 12 tons. As this is the weight at which the front axle has zero loading, apply the 60% as before and we have a SWL of approximately 8 tons.

Why bother, you may ask, with the expense of a six-wheeled vehicle which cannot do as much as a four wheeler. Well, first of all, let's consider the weight taken by that single axle. Taking again the moments about the front axle, we have:

$$(8 \text{ tons} \times 6 \text{ ft}) + (8 \text{ tons} \times 16 \text{ ft}) = 48 + 128 = 176 \text{ tons.ft}$$

$$\text{Dividing by the wheelbase} = \frac{176 \text{ tons.ft}}{12 \text{ ft}} = 14.7 \text{ tons}$$

—all on a 10 ton axle too!—and what's more, the whole rig is stationary and has not yet subjected itself to the shock forces met when moving along the road.

The difference between a four wheeler and the six wheeler is the overhang distance, particularly with a six wheeler with a four spring bogie due to the extra chassis length needed for the rear spring hangers—another good reason for the two spring traction bogie.

Well, can we improve the situation? The answer is—with a bit of thought—yes we can. Have another look at the six wheeler.

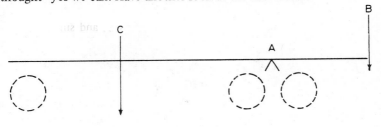

Figure 51

Dealing with moments is made easier if the train comprising the recovery vehicle and the casualty weight is considered as a beam, tipping about a pivot point or fulcrum, as shown in *Figure 51*. If we have a two spring bogie, the whole thing will tip about point A. That is, if a weight B is lifted, the truck will rotate about A and, if the weight is sufficient, the front axle will rise off the ground. At this juncture let's settle one argument, it doesn't matter *where* the crane is sited, it's only the overhang that is important.

So where are we! We have C, the weight of the recovery vehicle (acting through the centre of gravity) on one side of the see-saw, balancing (or failing to balance) the weight B of the casualty taken by crane. Going back to Chapter 8, we find that weight C multiplied by the distance A to C has to exceed the weight B multiplied by the distance A to B or the see-saw will tip on the side B. It does not matter if the see-saw tips on the side C because we have the front wheels acting as a snubber.

What can we do to improve the lifting capacity of the truck? Looking at *Figure 51* three things come to mind:

1. Cut the distance A to B (the overhang distance),
2. Increase the distance A to C (move the centre of gravity of the truck forward) and,
3. Increase the weight C (make the truck heavier).

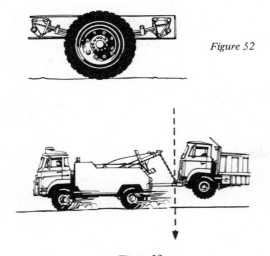

Figure 52

Figure 53

The overhang distance comprises two parts; the distance from the bogie centre to the end of the truck and the distance from the end of the truck to the lifting perpendicular. The first and simplest thing to do is to cut the chassis down to as close to the back of the rearmost tyre as possible, as shown in *Figure 52*. This would be difficult if you have a four spring bogie and the rear spring hanger to cope with. Alternatively, you can tuck the casualty as close as possible to your rear end, bearing in mind that corners have to be turned. Merely moving the crane forward, as in *Figure 53*, won't do. It cuts the perpendicular distance down, and in practice, you get the result shown in *Figure 53* and the effective perpendicular will then be the dotted line. So we're no better off.

In practice, it's probably better to choose the arrangement shown in *Figure 54*, where the perpendicular is still close (see the dotted line).

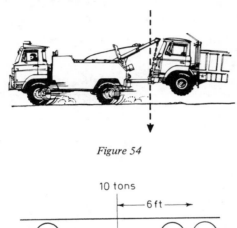

Figure 54

10 tons

←——6 ft——→

Figure 55

There is a tendency to push the casualty away from the rear and control whilst under braking is improved.

We have cut the overhang to a minimum and we must next increase the distance *A* to *C* (*Figure 51*), that is, move the centre of gravity further forward. This is a question of ballasting which takes care of the other item on the list—increasing the total weight of the truck. Let's assume that the total weight is 10 tons, acting 6 ft forward of the bogie centre (*Figure 55*). Now if we add, say 1 ton, 6 feet forward of the bogie we have only increased the weight and done nothing about shifting the C of G. Previously we had 10 tons × 6 ft = 60 ton.ft. and now we have 11 tons × 6 ft = 66 ton.ft.

If we place 1 ton of ballast 10 ft forward of the bogie we have:

	Weight	Distance	Moment
Truck	10	6	60
Ballast	1	10	10
	11 tons		70 tonf.ft

The centre of gravity is then 70 divided by 11 which equals 6.4 ft forward of the bogie, note the increase in moments from 66 ton.ft.

Have another attempt—take that 1 ton off again and put half of it in the front bumper position, say 4 feet forward of the front axle. What have we got? Take the moments about the bogie centre:

	Weight	Distance	Moment
Truck	10	6	60
Ballast	½	18	9
Total	10½ tons	24	69 tons.ft

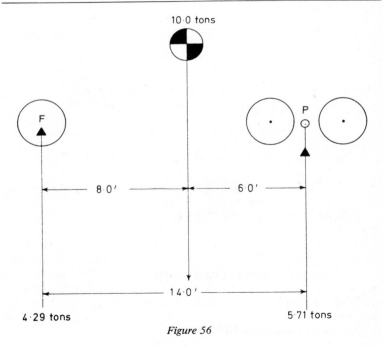

Figure 56

The centre of gravity is 69/10½ = 6.57 ft forward of the bogie. The important thing is, that with half the weight, we have, very nearly, the same result in 69 tons.ft. against the previously obtained 70 tons.ft.

There is one more bonus. Previously the 1 ton of ballast, being situated between the front and the rear axles, imposed a load on both. This is not always desirable as we need as much spare capacity from the rear axle(s) to carry the imposed load of the casualty. We therefore want to avoid putting too much weight on the rear axle(s).

When moving the ballast weight forward of the front axle, however, we actually unload the rear axle(s), thus allowing a greater crane lift before the maximum axle capacity is reached. Let's take a look at the kerb weight of the same truck, before and after (see *Figure 56*).

Before ballasting

C of G = 6 ft forward of bogie.
Wheelbase = 14 ft.
Total weight 10 tons.

Taking moments about the front axle F we have:

14 ft × P tons (where P is the axle load) will be balanced by 10 tons × 8 ft.

i.e. 14P tons ft = 80 tons.ft.

$$P = \frac{80 \text{ tons.ft}}{14 \text{ ft}} = 5.71 \text{ tons}$$

Total vehicle weight = 10.00 tons

Rear axles load   = 5.71 tons

Front axle load   = 4.29 tons

After ballasting (*Figure 57*)

C of G = 6.57 forward of bogie centre

W/B   = 14 ft.

Total vehicle weight = 10.5 tons.

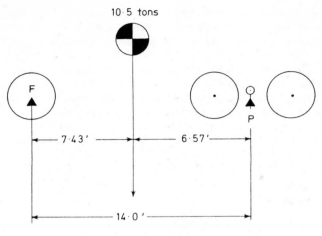

Figure 57

Taking the moments about the front axle as before:

14 ft × P tons   = 7.43 ft × 10.5 tons

$$P = \frac{7.43 \text{ ft} \times 10.5 \text{ tons}}{14 \text{ ft}}$$

= 5.57 tons

which is the new rear axle weight and the balance i.e. 10.5 tons − 5.57 tons = 4.93 tons is the new steering axle weight.

Compare the figures:

	Before	*After*	
F/A	4.29	4.93	+ 0.64 tons
R/A	5.71	5.57	− 0.14 tons
Total	10.00	10.50	+ 0.50 tons

The conclusion is, of course, that whilst adding useful ballast, you have actually taken weight off the bogie and loaded up the steering axle. This is fine as long as it's under the designed limit of the steering axle.

One final point about improving the performance of a recovery vehicle. Although we have done the three things that were required, that is, we have cut the overhang, pushed the C of G forward *and*

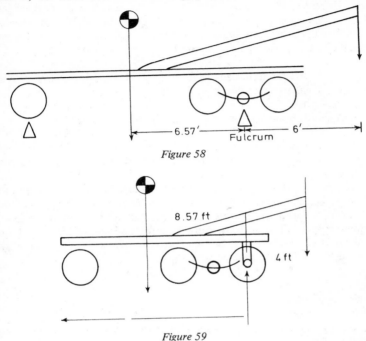

Figure 58

Figure 59

increased the weight, there is still one thing to do and this is to move the fulcrum. Look at *Figure 58* which shows the previous situation. Now look at *Figure 59*. By shifting the fulcrum back by 2 feet we have:

1. Extended the C of G distance and thus the moment (from 60 ton.ft to 80 ton.ft)
2. Cut the overhang from 6 ft to 4 ft. The lifting capability in both cases will be:

First: $\dfrac{60 \text{ tons.ft}}{6 \text{ ft}} = 10$ tons lift (zero front axle load)

Secondly: $\dfrac{80 \text{ tons.ft}}{4 \text{ ft}} = 20$ tons lift (zero front axle load)

How is it done? By inserting a stop—a wedge, block of steel, or hydraulic ram between the chassis and the third axle—the fulcrum point is shifted from the bogie trunnion to the centre of the rear axle. However, the unavoidable drawback is that the third axle takes 90% of the imposed load, thus turning a six wheeler into a four wheeler!

In practice, there are definite benefits in using a 6 wheeler provided that the operator is aware of the implications. These are:

1. A six wheel unit can cope with all normal loads and provide traction, especially with a third axle differential lock,
2. A 6-wheeler spreads the imposed axle loads over 2 axles.
3. There is more rubber on the road for braking purposes.

There are cases, in *emergencies*, when blocking the third axle will give the *apparent* benefits of the *theoretical* lifting ability of a four wheeler.

So long as the speed is kept down to an absolute minimum, and the distance likewise, it is possible to move very large weights from hazardous positions to positions of safety. It is for this reason that really heavy prime movers, 80 or so tons, can take imposed loads of 20 tons on one axle without fear of overloading. The wise man will always know the capabilities and limitations of his vehicle.

Selecting a chassis

Have a look at the chassis selection chart in the Appendix to this book. Having selected, hopefully, a suitable chassis the next question will be 'Is such a chassis available?' If so, go ahead and buy it.

Next assume the vehicle is standing in the yard, all fitted up with your favourite crane and winch. The bodywork a pure symphony as to design, the paint job a joy to behold. It's cost plenty, but as yet it is unable to do the simplest job. Now is the time to make with the back pocket to ensure that it will be able to. In Chapter 15 there is a short list giving the minimum requirements to do any kind of job at all. On top of this there will be a few specialist items. For instance, ever done any tanker work? If not, take a deep breath, for here we go again.

Chapter 12

TANKERS

Oil companies who own Tankers (or to be more exact Road Tank Waggons or RTW's) can be touchy about the recovery of their vehicles. Great exception is taken to bending a chassis, or to a wire rope which eventually creases a tank. It might, therefore, pay to do a little homework on tankers, their owners and the requirements demanded by law in relation to tankers.

The big worry about tankers—particularly those which carry hazardous cargoes, such as petroleum—is sparking. In order to avoid this, the regulations are quite severe. For example:

(a) Double pole wiring must be fitted.
(b) The wiring must be continuous.
(c) A master switch must be fitted which isolates the battery and also the field windings of the generator.
(d) If a battery is carried behind the flame shield, it must be placed in a steel box which extends downwards to within 12 in of the ground.
(e) The exhaust pipe must emit in front of the flame shield.
(f) The vehicle must be fitted with a diesel engine.

If, after all this has been done, there is a leak to earth of more than 15 milliamps, the tanker will not be allowed to load.

Very stringent regulations control the operation of tankers, and equally stringent regulations apply in the case of an accident. We must, therefore, help ourselves by adopting some of the standards laid down. For example, if called out to a tanker accident, don't bother if you are the proud owner of a petrol driven vehicle.

All running lights on a tanker are of the vapour proof variety, and working lights, including torches, must be of the Home Office approved pattern. So don't go running about with a tin torch, or even a rubber one for that matter.

A FEW HINTS

1. Don't walk around a crippled tanker with a lighted cigarette.
2. If the tanker requires more than a wheel change, *don't touch it* until either the Fire Brigade or a Company Representative arrives on the scene. The latter will probably ask quite a few questions about your equipment, and will certainly want to know the extent of your insurance. Carry the necessary documents about with you. The Company Representative will probably be quite knowledgeable; he will know about Safe Working Loads of wire, chains and the like. He will take exception to your putting a winch wire around his tanker, and may demand that more sophisticated gear is used, for instance, a wide, nylon strop. He will be very fussy about sparks and will suggest that chains and shackles should be carried and not thrown around as usual.

   Don't drive your wedges in with a club hammer. A copper mallet will be preferred.

HAZCHEM

Nowadays, there is a clever system called Hazchem. This is designed to help to determine what a tanker is carrying, and what to do about it. Each vehicle carries a marker board or sticker indicating visually the type of substance being carried. A translation of the code is given in the Tables in Appendix 2.

Chapter 13

EQUIPMENT AND DEVICES

TOWBARS

These have already been described as potentially dangerous bits of
equipment—and, make no mistake—they are. However, certain circumstances make the use of towbars unavoidable. Many operators prefer
to use a straight bar because it is easier to handle and, admittedly, one
doesn't have to crawl underneath a casualty and lay on one's back
to fit one. However, a swan-necked bar offers considerable benefits.

Figure 60

Figure 61

In *Figure 60* the direction of effort is along the line of the straight
bar but in *Figure 61* the direction of effort is along the dotted line
joining axle to the towing jaw. Think back to two chapters ago where

we were trying to winch a truck whose front wheel was up against a brick? The same principle applies here, except that here we call it the Angle of Friction.

In practical terms the angle of friction could be determined by placing a vehicle on a variable ramp and adjusting same until the truck was about to move. The angle between the ramp and the ground would be the angle of friction. Naturally in the case of a truck the angle is quite a shallow one.

There is an added bonus when using the swan-necked bar. The reaction to your pull tries to pull the towing jaws out in the direction of the dotted line (*Figure 61*), and this puts extra weight on the Recovery Vehicle's drive bogie, which is exactly what you want to increase traction to get the load moving. Disadvantages? Of course, there always are, have you tried lifting a swan-necked bar single handed?

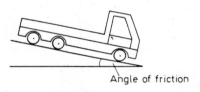

Angle of friction

Figure 62

Incidentally, the angle of friction also applies when winching, and it should be possible to arrange the layout so as to take advantage of this phenomenon (*Figure 61*).

V-BARS AND A-BARS

Generally speaking, a V-bar is the same as an A-bar except that it is used on the opposite direction, as shown in *Figure 63*.

Obviously, much more control is possible with either of these bars, but when they 'break away' they do so with alarming suddenness to the detriment of both casualty and recovery vehicle and any passing traffic, etc. If a lifting eye, or eyes are arranged at the casualty end of the bar, a lift and tow is possible and if using a twin-lift crane, the tension on each of the cables will serve to control any sudden 'break-away'.

A better idea is a fully tracking V-bar and, for a lift and tow, a combination bar and spreader. Here, instead of two points of contact being fixed and the other one totally free, we have four fully articulating joints (see *Figure 64*). The two at the casualty end are closer

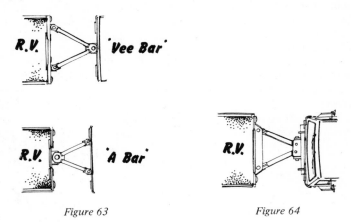

Figure 63   Figure 64

together than those at the recovery vehicle end, thus giving complete tracking because the recovery vehicle on turning a corner, puts compressive forces on to the inside bar (*Figure 65*). The turning point is around A and the towing tension set up in the outside bar. This control is further assisted with twin lift cranes. Note that all four points have to

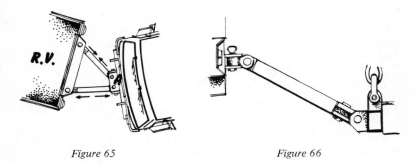

Figure 65   Figure 66

be free in the horizontal plane and, taking a look at the side view (*Figure 66*) all points have to be free in the vertical plane.

Just a small point. When using chains to a casualty in conjunction with either a V-bar, an A-bar, or whatever, consider the forces involved.

Have a look at the chain in *Figure 66*, particularly at the point A where it changes direction.

Suppose for example, you are lifting 5 tons. This one chain would then be supporting half that, ie 2½ tons. Note that we say *supporting* 2½ tons. This does not mean that the load on the chain *is* 2½ tons.

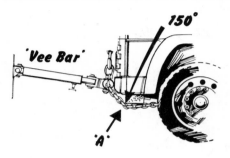

Figure 67

Have another look at the diagram, and consider the angle at A. It could be 150°, or even more in certain circumstances. Refer back to the table on page 14 concerning 2 leg brothers, and you will see that a load of 2½ tons at 150° causes a load in each leg of around 4¾ tons. The only answer is to keep the angle to a minimum, and use an appropriate chain.

With bars of any kind, never use the eyes sometimes provided by the vehicle manufacturer for a lift and tow. Many people are afraid of using eyes, even for towing.

Another thing when towing, or lift and towing: ensure that the propshaft of the casualty is disconnected. The reason for this is, that some gearboxes, when in neutral, have no drive to the oil pump, and thus lack the necessary lubrication. In our case, of course, the propshaft, if it is still connected, turns the gears, which may in time seize up, or have been known to start the engine of the casualty.

TOWBOGIE

Another method of lift and towing appliance is the patent 'Towbogie'. This is a cradle device which is 'clipped' over the front axle of the casualty, and lifted at the other end by the crane of the recovery vehicle, a fulcrum being provided by means of a block (or blocks) of wood arranged under the spring hangers or front chassis closing member. Naturally, the position of the wood block determines the amount of downwards thrust on the front axle, thus tending to open the springs which later should be chained to the chassis (don't forget the wedges!) before lifting takes place.

This method effectively lengthens the wheelbase of the casualty vehicle, thus lessening the load to be taken by the crane, and again reducing the axle loading of the Recovery Vehicle. Take, for example, a truck, a four wheeler, with a 12 ft wheelbase and a front axle loading of 5 tons. The length of the towbogie is 5 ft and thus the new wheelbase becomes 17 ft. What is the load to be taken by the crane? Taking moments about A, the rear axle we have:

$$\frac{12 \text{ ft} \times 5 \text{ tons}}{17 \text{ ft}} = \text{Weight taken by crane} = \frac{60 \text{ ton.ft}}{17 \text{ ft}} = 3\frac{1}{2} \text{ tons approx.}$$

Problems will arise if care is not taken over the positioning of the wood block and if the spring support chains are not properly wedged.

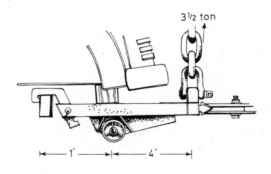

Figure 68

Take, for example, the case where the wood is placed too close to the axle as in *Figure 68*. Assume, for the time being, that we have exerted a load of 3½ tons as before on the device and, taking moments about the fulcrum we have:

$$\frac{4 \text{ ft} \times 3\frac{1}{2} \text{ tons}}{1 \text{ ft}} = \text{downward thrust on the axle} = 14 \text{ tons}$$

This is a bit much.

Translate half this thrust to terms of pressure on a badly adjusted chain over the chassis member and you may be taking the whole of the 14 tons on one of them!

When towing with a lifted vehicle, considerable weight can be relieved from V-bars and the like by inclining lifting chains or cables outwards. This will reduce bumping and justling when stopping, for example, at traffic lights.

NYLON STROP

The wide (10 in–12 in) nylon or Terylene strop is an expensive, but most useful piece of equipment. It will probably have a triangular link at each end to receive a shackle. Even the delicate aluminium or fibreglass covering of tankers can withstand the pressures applied by these strops. Take, for example, a 5 ton pull on such a strop. Wrapped around a tank casing it would have to be about 14 ft long, with perhaps 7ft in contact. If it is 10 in wide, we have 84 in $\times$ 10 in = 840 in^2 of area to take the 5 tons, which comes out at $11,200 \, lb/840 = 13 \, lbf/sq. in.$ Even if only one strop is used the pressure will be greater in that area directly opposite the direction of effort; but even twice as much is tolerable. Such a strop, and ideally, two are required, costs over £50. Each strop should be carefully looked after, should be kept clean and for preference, stowed in its own canvas bag.

BULLDOG GRIPS

If you are unable to splice wire rope properly, make a 'Yankee eye splice' with three bulldog grips. Some people may know them by a

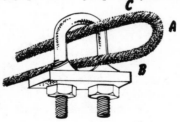

Figure 69

different name but they are these gadgets that have two parts; one part is a small U bolt, complete with nuts, and the second part is a saddle with two holes necessary for the U bolt (see *Figure 69*).

Note that the U bolt is fitted over the 'standing part' of the rope and the saddle fitted over the short end. To do the job neatly, the wire should be seized to the thimble at A, B and C, doing A first. The grips can then be fitted, one of them nice and snug up to the tail of the thimble. Like wheel nuts, but even more so, each one should be tightened up one turn at a time, and in the later stages, half a turn before going to its neighbour.

THE 'DONALDSON' REACTOR

This is a device invented by Mr Donaldson for the Army when it was found that when going up steep hills, there was a distinct lack of steering when pulling a heavy lift and tow (see *Figure 70*). This is due to the Centre of Gravity effectively being moved towards the rear axle, thus lightening the load on the steering axle. This transfers the load to the rear axle and, in many cases overloads it.

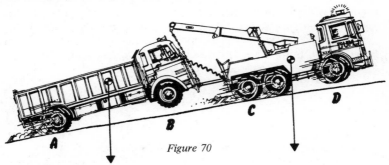

Figure 70

Essentially Mr Donaldson's idea was to join the two outside axles of the whole rig, A to D, with a substantial wire rope, and to shorten the rope. Naturally this would increase the load on A and D and at the same time decrease the load on B, and thus on C. The trick is in shortening the rope, and was solved by connecting the cable not to the front axle but to a hydraulic ram and so, at the touch of a finger, the required load could be transferred. In fact the exact load could be transferred by incorporating a suitably calibrated pressure gauge in the system.

Other problems arise when turning corners or when going over the brow of hills and so an hydraulic accumulator is incorporated to relax and then take up the tension again. Also, to avoid the cable fouling wheels, etc when turning corners a set of rollers and guides is built onto the recovery vehicle exactly below the point of the vee bar articulation. Expensive? Yes, but it works! In fact a very serious scientific paper hailed the idea as being aesthetically and geometrically the best since Archimedes!

KNOWING WHEN TO STOP

This might seem to be an unnecessary thing to write about, but, unfortunately, most people hate to be beaten. Of course, if a truck is broken down and immovable, someone has to move it, some time. Why should it not be you, with the equipment and the knowledge.

Perhaps it will be thought necessary to unload the casualty first. This will take extra time, but might save hundreds of pounds of damage. If the police insist that road clearance is the first priority then the cargo may not get damaged but use your initiative to keep this to the minimum.

For example, take the case of a loaded tanker which cannot be moved without a rear end lift. It is highly desirable to unload first particularly if the cargo is a dangerous one. Even if your vehicle can take a load of up to 15 tons (which will be necessary to lift the rear end of a loaded eight wheeler), look at the load that is being transferred to the front axles. Let's assume we have a 30 tonner (see *Figure 71*).

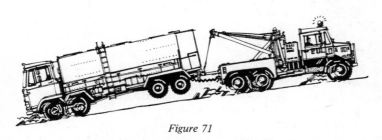

Figure 71

If the hook load is 15 tons and the total weight is 30 tons, then the other 15 tons is pressing down on the front axles. This would not be so bad if there was equal load on the two, but there isn't because having lifted the rear end you have started to take the weight off the second axle and so the bulk of the 15 tons will come onto the front axle. Therefore the solution is, if you have to move the vehicle, unload it first or have it unloaded. If this is not possible, then lift it as little as possible and move it very slowly to the nearest layby and then leave it until it can be unloaded.

It is worthwhile mentioning the loads that the chassis will be taking; the nearest parallel is that of a beam, made initially to be a span of 15 ft supported at each end. The beam has been designed to cope with this load (see *Figure 72*). Now assume that someone comes along and kicks away one set of supports and puts in another 6 ft away. You now have an unsupported span of 21 ft.

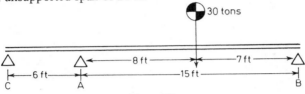

Figure 72

The bending moment in the first case (about A) is $30 \times 8 = 240$ ton.ft. In the second case, the bending moment, still about A, will be $30 \times 14 = 420$ ton.ft. Thus, the chances are that the beam, or in our case the chassis, will bend, so it might have been cheaper to have had the truck unloaded, or part unloaded, first. Of course, somebody may come up with the bright idea of stiffening the chassis with an RSJ or two to give support. This will require careful work, using good chains, and plenty of them, with, of course, swags of wedges, ending up with something like *Figure 73*.

Figure 73

This may be a fairly long job and it might be quicker to unload. The point we are trying to make is that it is always best to know when to stop and call in help.

'GEAR STRETCHING'

This is the gentle pastime whose chief adherents belong to the 'Pull Anything' club. This type of operator is easily recognised by a vast profusion of broken chains, bent shackles, and wires looking like bunches of grapes.

However, there are certain circumstances where gear can be used to the limit, when, for example, a life can be saved. Even then, it is only permissible to put half the breaking strain on any piece of equipment. It is therefore essential to know what the breaking strain is. If this strain is put on chains and shackles, they should be sent back to the chainworks to be annealed and re-tested. In the case of wire rope, a thorough examination, oiling and, above all, resting for up to three months is necessary. There is no excuse for damaged equipment; its causes are ignorance or misjudgement and its effects are always expensive and sometimes lethal.

Chapter 14

DERRICK CRANES

A derrick is a boom supported at its lower end by a swivel pin or gooseneck, and at its upper end supported by one end of a topping lift. In turn, the stem end of the topping lift is supported by a king post (*Figure 74*).

This system is probably one of the oldest types of crane known to man, and very efficient it is too, particularly when the topping lift is adjustable so as to set the height and reach of the boom.

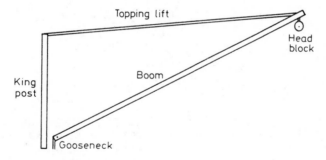

Figure 74

Naturally, the boom can be swung from side to side usually by guys fitted at either side of the boom head. The use of this type of crane with the booms in pairs are well known in the Recovery Vehicle application.

Like every such system, there are one or two snags which have to be recognised and dealt with. The first snag is the situation of the gooseneck, which, if not sited directly beneath the support point of the topping lift, a moment of force about the gooseneck will be created as the boom is swung over the side and the boom will swing in the direction of the arrow (*Figure 75*) until something, usually the cab, stops it.

This is what the guys are for, but very rarely seen in recovery vehicle applications. If they are used however, another snag develops because the moment of force is still there trying to swing the boom, which in this case is being restrained and therefore the boom will try and bend.

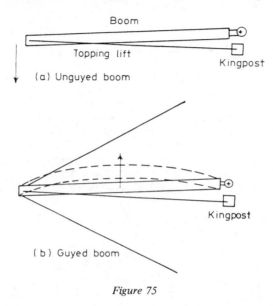

Figure 75

The forces acting upon each member of the crane alter as the angle of the boom is altered, from the horizontal. So let us examine these forces the better to get the very best results from such a crane. Naturally enough, the height of the king post and the length of the boom are important to the calculations.

Moment of Force calculations

In *Figure 76* KP is the king post, which for the purpose of example is 6 ft high. TP is the boom, and is 16 ft long, inclined at an angle of 35 degrees to the horizontal.

A winch is sited at the foot of the boom and the rope is rove directly through a block at the head of the boom (T).

For the sake of simplicity, as all the loadings are proportional, let us lift a load of 10 tons, thus a load of 1 ton will set up loadings of one tenth of those found here, and so a load of x tons will set us $x/10$ tons of loading in all the members.

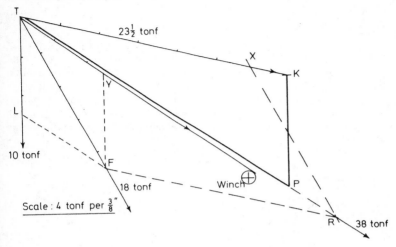

Figure 76. Simple lift of 10 tonf. Wire rove direct through head block

Let's get on with it. 10 tons is lifted, therefore there is a 10 ton load on the line TL, therefore a load of 10 tons is taken by the same rope, indicated by the line TY. Note that they are both scaled on the sketch at 4 tonf per $3/8$ in. Each line is therefore about one inch long.

Complete the parallelogram by drawing YF parallel to TL; and LF parallel to TY. The length of the line TF (at the same scale of ¼ in per ton) is the amount of force taken by the head block, and the direction of TF is also the direction of the force. In our sketch, the force works out at 18 tons; which, when you come to think of it, is a bit severe when you only want to lift 10 tons. This, so they say, is life. Just make sure that a suitable block is used.

TF, then, is the resultant force of the two forces TL and TY which are acting upon our block. As it is the resultant, it may replace the other two. Let us work with it.

We now want to find the force in the topping lift TK and the force-thrust-in the boom, TP. If FR is drawn parallel to the topping lift TK and RX is drawn parallel to TF from the point where FR crosses the line of the boom, a new parallelogram TFRX is formed, the diagonal TR, being the thrust in tons in the boom, and the line TX being the loading on the topping span. Using the same scale as before, we find that the boom thrust—all taken by the way, on the gooseneck—is 38 tons, and that the topping lift is subjected to a load of 23½ tons.

Reducing the loads

There is, however, a very clever way of reducing the loads on the boom and topping lift, and is a very good example of the triumph of mind over matter, or what really can be done when the brain is engaged.

Now consider the diagram in *Figure 77*. Only a small alteration has been made. The lifting rope, instead of being rove straight through the head block, has first been taken to a block sited at the top of the king post.

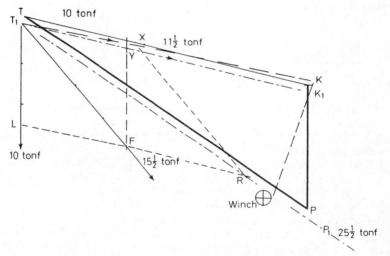

Figure 77. Simple lift of 10 tonf. Wire rove through head block via king post head

The analysis of the forces is carried out in the same way as before. The load is still 10 tons, and the line TF is the resultant force set up at the head block. Note that T was created so as to keep the drawing as simple as possible, so that the line T_1P_1 is parallel to the boom and thus accurately represents the forces upon it.

The new resultant force is 15½ tons. In a similar manner, as before, the thrust upon the boom gooseneck is found to be 25½ tons, and the force imposed upon the topping lift is found to be only 11½ tons.

Compare the results in the table below:

	Figure 76	Figure 77
Lift	10 tons	10 tons
Head Block	18 tons	15½ tons
Boom	38 tons	25½ tons
Topping Lift	23½ tons	11½ tons

A remarkable reduction has been achieved by allowing the lifting rope to share the strain with the topping lift.

However, danger, for the unwary is waiting around the corner. Suppose, just suppose, that for the sake of safety and because of previous exhortations, one considered it necessary to reduce the load

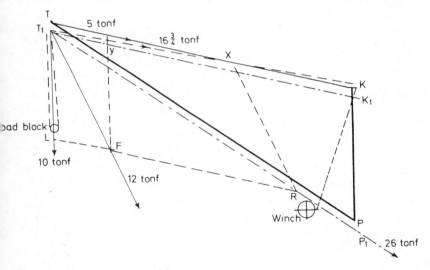

Figure 78. Compound lift of 10 tonf. Wire rove through head and load block via king post head

on the winch rope by reeving a double reduction at the lift by the inclusion of a snatch block. The only thing to pat your back would probably be the boom itself, and most heartily indeed. Consider the diagram in Figure 78 and note that the only difference from Figure 77 is the snatch block at L.

Again, a weight of 10 tons is being lifted; but due to the fact that a snatch block has been introduced there is only a force of 5 tons being taken by the winch rope. Complete the parallelogram TYFL and note that the resultant TF is now reduced to 12 tons. Again, complete the parallelogram TFRX where the thrust upon the topping lift is found to be 16¾ tons. This is the important bit. Due to the snatch block, the help given by the lifting rope to the topping lift is reduced, and thus the topping lift must take an increased load.

This is all well and good if the topping lift is strong enough to take the load but there is another factor.

Consider the very head of the boom where the topping lift is joined, usually by a lug, welded or strapped, to the boom.

The boom can take a considerable thrust in the direction indicated by T in Figure 79, but the topping lift imposes a bending moment upon the boom about the lug, and the extra force put upon the topping lift can create a sufficient force to cause the boom to bend.

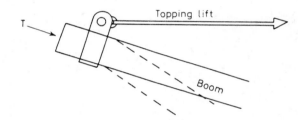

Figure 79. Topping lift

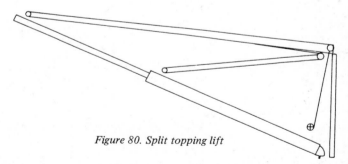

Figure 80. Split topping lift

Naturally, a further increase of weight upon the topping lift can be caused by introducing yet another snatch block into the lifting line.

In most recovery cranes of this type, the booms are usually short, and moreover constructed so that they are thicker in the middle so as to take into account these extra stresses. The trouble only arises if the boom is lengthened by having an extending boom, which is not so strengthened. In this case it will probably be better to rearrange the topping lift to make a support for the centre of the (extended) boom, and at the same time halving the load at the boom head (*Figure 80*).

The foregoing could well cause you to agree that every recovery vehicle should have this notice, suitably mounted, put into the cab.

'Brain should be engaged before mouth or other equipment is operated.'

Chapter 15

SAFETY AND LEGISLATION

Most people will agree that there is little merit in arriving fully equipped, both in knowledge and equipment, and getting killed in the process for want of a small portion of common sense. Imagine going home one night, in winter, pouring with rain, doing at least 50 miles an hour and just coming up to a bend. Halfway round the bend you are confronted by a recovery vehicle, stopped at the side of the road and illuminated by all the incandescent brilliance of a proud, yellow, rotating beacon. Whilst you have a busy few seconds with brakes and steering, you happen to notice the white faces of the Recovery Crew. Under the circumstances a white face may be understandable, but as a method of illumination leaves a lot to be desired. A set of black oilskins surmounted by a white face cannot be said to be the last word in advertising one's presence. And yet, it happens all the time.

Your shopping list should contain the following essential items:

9 fluourescent traffic cones;
2 yellow battery-operated flashing lamps;
1 fluorescent Accident sign. Blue background, white letters;
1 'Dayglow' waistcoat for each man;
1 white fluorescent safety hat;
Half-a-dozen coins for the telephone;
The telephone number of your Local Police Traffic Department.

So that there is no misunderstanding, let's get one or two things straight. For the purposes of clarity, there are four instances where your services will be required.

1. *Accident on Motorway.* You will be called in only by the Police.
2. *Breakdown on Motorway.* You will again be called in by the Police, on the request of the stranded driver.

3. *Accident on normal road.* You will most probably be called in by the Police.
4. *Breakdown on normal road.* You will be called in by the stranded driver.

In the first two cases, the motorway jobs, all signing and preliminary work will have already been done most efficiently to laid down Regulations, and it will be a very bold and foolish operator who tries to interfere. The chances of 'coming across' a casualty on a motorway are rare to the point of suspicion. We can confine ourselves, in the main, to breakdowns on minor roads.

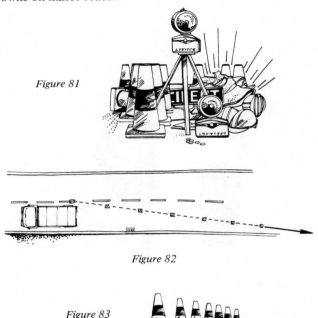

Figure 81

Figure 82

Figure 83

First rule is to post your *Accident* sign as far back down the road as possible. The second rule is to remind people of the first sign, and the third rule is to 'come off' the area in such a manner that the cones appear as a 'wall of cones'. A typical layout might be shown in *Figure 82*. Look how the cones have been arranged in a taper, so that the driver is confronted by the wall of cones. The driver's view will be as in *Figure 83*.

Rule four, and perhaps the most important, is that if you find your-self in a tricky situation as above, phone the traffic department and request assistance. They will be very pleased to help. Don't forget that any accident that results from your blocking the road will be blamed on you. Rule five is to use your headlights.

PERSONAL SAFETY

The above will serve to warn a driver that trouble is in the area and, if you are lucky, he might slow down enough to miss your recovery vehicle. The best policy is to be seen; Dayglo waistcoats are fairly cheap and should be worn—always. To date it has been the vogue to wear the well-known Recovery Operator's uniform of overalls, black

Figure 84

oilskins, wellington boots and often a woollen hat. The overalls may be OK, but replace the wellingtons with boots with steel toecaps (very handy when a shackle falls on your toe) and replace the woolly hat with a hard one. Again, for safety's sake, learn a system of signals and make sure your mate learns them as well. These are displayed in *Figure 85*.

The following signals should be learned and never forgotten:

Signals to lower away   (crane) Touch head—point down
    ,,   ,, lift   (crane) Touch head—point up
    ,,   ,, heave in   (winch)
    ,,   ,, ease out   (winch)
    ,,   ,, hold on (stop) (winch and crane)

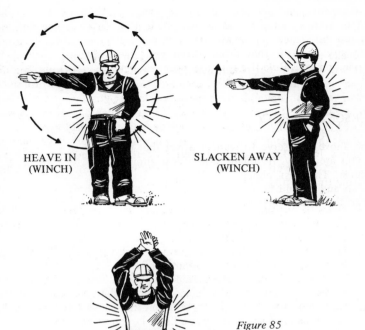

HEAVE IN
(WINCH)

SLACKEN AWAY
(WINCH)

Figure 85

HOLD FAST
(CRANE AND WINCH)

A final word. At the beginning of the book, mention was made of carrying a notebook and pencil, and now we can add a 'Polaroid' camera. These items are for your protection. If there are problems in three month's time about the damage that you caused, you will have notes *and* photograph to prove your point. All the items mentioned are expensive but then so is the property that you are recovering.

LEGISLATION

Despite a multiplicity of laws, there are many grey areas where blame, in the event of an accident, may be apportioned. Our enthusiastic operator may find himself in court being asked several pertinent, and even impertinent, questions as to his behaviour, and to that of the vehicle supposedly under his control. It will be little use him quoting the law about exempt vehicles if his 5 cwt van fails to stop a loaded 8-wheeler that he has been towing—even at 5 miles an hour.

It will help if your chain, wire, and shackle test certificates are up to date and valid. It is also a very good idea to ensure that your Insurance Broker really understands the type of work that you do, and the risks and the amounts that may be involved if you accidentally drop a tanker full of LPG which catches fire and then decimates a small town.

There are excellent books written about transport law, such as Kitchin's Road Transport Law (Butterworths). Make sure you have read them. There are, however, a few questions and answers which crop up from time to time which may be useful:

1. Does the driver of a recovery vehicle have to possess an HGV licence? Yes, he does, for the type of vehicle that he is *driving*, (as opposed to towing).
2. Does the chap in the towed vehicle have to have an HGV? No. He does not need a licence of any kind.
3. What about towing articulated vehicles? Loaded artics may be towed with a recovery vehicle, provided that the length of the train does not exceed 18 m, and that the recovery vehicle weighs 7.25 tons or more, thus being a Light Locomotive.
4. When may flashing amber lamps be used? Nowadays you can use them going to, at, and coming away from an accident.
5. Does a recovery vehicle have to possess a test Certificate? No, it doesn't.

APPENDICES

Appendix 1

HAZCHEM CARD

Hazchem Scale

FOR FIRE OR SPILLAGE

| Hazchem | | Issue No 1 |
| UN No | | |

1	JETS	
2	FOG	
3	FOAM	
4	DRY AGENT	

P	V	FULL	
R			
S	V	BA	DILUTE
S		BA for FIRE only	
T		BA	
T		BA for FIRE only	
W	V	FULL	
X			
Y	V	BA	CONTAIN
Y		BA for FIRE only	
Z		BA	
Z		BA for FIRE only	

| **E** | CONSIDER EVACUATION |

Notes for Guidance

FOG

In the absence of fog equipment a
fine spray may be used.

DRY AGENT

Water **must not** be allowed to come
into contact with the substance at risk.

V

Can be violently or even explosively
reactive.

FULL

Full body protective clothing with BA.

BA

Breathing apparatus plus protective gloves.

DILUTE

May be washed to drain with large
quantities of water.

CONTAIN

Prevent, by any means available, spillage
from entering drains or water course.

Appendix 2

HAZCHEM CODE

ALLOCATION OF HAZCHEM CODING
(Joint Committee on Fire Brigade Operations.
Hazchem Working Party – Technical sub-committee)

Note: > = greater than; < = less than.

U.N. Number	Substance	Hazchem Code	U.N. Label
1005	Ammonia, anhydrous and solutions >50%	2PE	Toxic gas
1010	Butadiene	3WE	Inflammable gas
1011	Butane	3WE	Inflammable gas
1012	Butylene (Butane)	3WE	Inflammable gas
1017	Chlorine	2XE	Toxic gas
1032	Dimethylamine (Anhydrous)	2PE	Inflammable gas
1037	Ethyl chloride (Chlorethane)	3WE	Inflammable gas
1040	Ethylene oxide	2WE	Inflammable gas
1050	Hydrogen chloride (Anhydrous)	2RE	Toxic gas
1055	Isobutylene (Isobutane)	3WE	Inflammable gas
1062	Methyl bromide (Bromomethane)	2XE	Toxic gas
1063	Methyl chloride (Chloromethane)	3WE	Inflammable gas
1067	Nitrogen dioxide (Nitrogen Tetroxide) liquefied	2RE	Toxic gas
1076	Phosgene (Carbonyl chloride)	2XE	Toxic gas

1077	Propylene (Propane)	3WE	Inflammable gas
1079	Sulphur dioxide, liquefied	2RE	Toxic gas
1086	Vinyl chloride, inhibited	3WE	Inflammable gas
1090	Acetone	2$\boxed{S}$E	Inflammable liquid
1095	Acrylonitrile, inhibited	3WE	Inflammable liquid
1104	Amyl acetates	3$\boxed{Y}$	Inflammable liquid
1105	Amyl alcohols–primary and secondary	3$\boxed{Y}$	Inflammable liquid
1108	Amylene, normal (1–Pentene)	3$\boxed{Y}$ E	Inflammable liquid
1114	Benzene (Benzol)	3WE	Inflammable liquid
1120	2-Butanol (Butyl alcohols)	3$\boxed{Y}$	Inflammable liquid
1121	Secondary Butanol (Secondary Butyl alcohol)	2$\boxed{S}$	Inflammable liquid
1122	Tertiary Butanol (Tertiary Butyl alcohol)	2$\boxed{S}$E	Inflammable liquid
1123	Butyl acetate, normal	3$\boxed{Y}$	Inflammable liquid
1124	Secondary Butyl acetate	3$\boxed{Y}$ E	Inflammable liquid
1131	Carbon disulphide (Carbon bisulphide)	3WE	Inflammable liquid
1154	Chlorobenzene	2	
1134	Chlorobenzene (Monochlorobenzene)	2Y	Inflammable liquid
1145	Cyclohexane	3$\boxed{Y}$ E	Inflammable liquid
1146	Cyclopentane	3$\boxed{Y}$ E	Inflammable liquid
1147	Decahydronaphthalene (Decalin)	3$\boxed{Z}$	Inflammable liquid
1149	Dibutyl ethers (Butyl ethers)	3$\boxed{Y}$	Inflammable liquid
1155	Diethyl ether (Ethyl ether, Anaesthetic ether, Sulphuric ether)	3YE	Inflammable liquid
1157	2-6 dimothylheptan-4-one	3$\boxed{Y}$	Inflammable liquid
1159	Di-isopropyl ether	3$\boxed{Y}$ E	Inflammable liquid

1160	Dimethylamine solution	2PE	Inflammable liquid
1165	Dioxane	2SE	Inflammable liquid
1170	Ethanol (Ethyl alcohol)	2⒮E	Inflammable liquid
1172	2-Ethoxy ethyl acetate (Ethylene glycol mono-ethyl ether acetate)	2⒮	Inflammable liquid
1175	Ethyl acetate	3ⓎE	Inflammable liquid
1175	Ethyl benzene	3ⓎE	Inflammable liquid
1180	Ethyl-n-butyrate	3Ⓨ	Inflammable liquid
1190	Ethyl formate	3YE	Inflammable liquid
1193	Ethyl methyl ketone (Methyl ethyl ketone)	2⒮E	Inflammable liquid
1195	Ethyl propionate	3ⓎE	Inflammable liquid
1198	Formaldehyde in solutions (For example: Formalin)	2SE	Inflammable liquid
1203	Motor Spirit (includes Gasoline or Petrol)	3ⓎE	Inflammable liquid
1206	Heptane and its isomers	3ⓎE	Inflammable liquid
1208	Hexane and its isomers	3ⓎE	Inflammable liquid
1212	Isobutanol (Isobutyl alcohol)	3Ⓨ	Inflammable liquid
1213	Iso Butyl acetate	3ⓎE	Inflammable liquid
1216	Iso octene	3ⓎE	Inflammable liquid
1218	Isoprene, inhibited	3ⓎE	Inflammable liquid
1219	Isopropanol (Isopropyl alcohol)	2⒮E	Inflammable liquid
1220	Isopropyl acetate	3ⓎE	Inflammable liquid
1223	Kerosene (Paraffin)	3Ⓨ	Inflammable liquid
1229	Mesityl oxide	3W	Inflammable liquid
1230	Methanol (Methyl alcohol, Wood alcohol, Columbian spirits)	2PE	Inflammable liquid
1231	Methyl acetate	2⒮E	Inflammable liquid

1243	Methyl formate	2SE	Inflammable liquid
1247	Methyl methacrylate monomer, inhibited	3Y E	Inflammable liquid
1248	Methyl propionate	3Y E	Inflammable liquid
1251	Methyl Vinyl ketone	2PE	Inflammable liquid
1262	Octane and its isomers	3Y E	Inflammable liquid
1265	n-Pentane and isopentane	3Y E	Inflammable liqdid
1270	Petroleum fuel	3Y E	Inflammable liquid
1271	Petroleum spirit (Benzolene, Lythene, Petroleum ether)	3Y E	Inflammable liquid
1274	Propanol	2S E	Inflammable liquid
1276	Propyl acetate, normal	3Y E	Inflammable liquid
1282	Pyridine	2WE	Inflammable liquid
1292	Tetraethyl silicate (Ethyl silicate)	3Y	Inflammable liquid
1294	Toluene (Toluol)	3Y E	Inflammable liquid
1297	Trimethylamine, aqueous solutions containing not more than 30% of trimethylamine	2PE	Inflammable liquid
1299	Turpentine	3Y	Inflammable liquid
1300	Turpentine substitute (White spirit)	3Y	Inflammable liquid
1301	Vinyl acetate, inhibited	3Y E	Inflammable liquid
1307	Xylenes (Xylol)	3Y	Inflammable liquid
1334	Napthalene (solid) Crude or refined	2Z	Inflammable solid
1338	Phosphorus, Amorphous (Red Phosphorus)	2WE	Inflammable solid
1350	Sulphur	2Z	Inflammable solid
1381	Phosphorus, white or yellow, dry or under water or in solution	2WE	Spontaneously combustible
1428	Sodium metal	4W	Dangerous when wet

1486	Potassium nitrate (Saltpetre)	2▯	Oxidising substance
1498	Sodium nitrate (Chile Saltpetre)	2▯	Oxidising substance
1500	Sodium nitrite	2▨	Oxidising substance
1541	Acetone cyanohydrin	2XE	Poison
1547	Aniline (Aniline oil, phenylamine, Amino-benzene)	3X	Poison
1580	Chloropiorin (Trichloro-nitromethane)	2XE	Poison
1595	Dimethyl sulphate (Methyl sulphate)	2XE	Poison
1648	Methyl cyanide (Acenitrile)	2WE	Poison
1662	Nitrobenzene (Nitrobenzol, Mirbane oil)	2X	Poison
1671	Phenol (Carbolic acid) (Solid and aqueous solutions)	2X	Poison
1680	Potassium cyanide	4X	Poison
1689	Sodium cyanide	4X	Poison
1715	Acetic anhydride	2P	Corrosive
1717	Acetyl chloride	4WE	Corrosive
1726	Aluminium chloride anhydrous	4X	Corrosive
1730	Antimony pentachloride (Antimony perchloride) liquid	4X	Corrosive
1736	Benzoyl chloride	2X	Corrosive
1744	Bromine and solutions of bromine	2XE	Corrosive
1751	Chloroacetic acids, solid	2R	Corrosive
1754	Chlorosulphomic acid (with or	4WE	Corrosive
1789	Hydrochloric acid (Nuriatic acid, Spirits of salts) in solution	2R	Corrosive
1790	Hydrofluoric acid solution	2RE	Corrosive
1791	Hypochlorite, solutions containing more than 5% available chlorine	2R	Corrosive

1805	Phosphoric acid (ortho-phosphoric acid)	2E	Corrosive
1809	Phosphorus Trichloride	4WE	Corrosive
1810	Phosphorus Oxyxhloride	4WE	Corrosive
1813	Potassium hydroxide solid	2E	Corrosive
1814	Potassium hydroxide solution (Caustic potash, Potash liquor)	2E	Corrosive
1825	Sodium hydroxide, solid	2E	Corrosive
1824	Sodium hydroxide solution (Caustic soda liquor, Sodium hydrate, Lye)	2R	Corrosive
1829	Sulphur Trioxide inhibited	4WE	Corrosive
1830	Sulphuric acid	2P	Corrosive
1831	Sulphuric acid—fuming (01.one)	4WE	Corrosive
1832	Sulphuric acid spent	2R	Corrosive
1834	Sulphuryl chloride	4WE	Corrosive
1838	Titanium tetrachloride	4XE	Corrosive
1915	Cyclohexanons	3Ⓨ	Inflammable liquid
1918	Isopropylbenzene (Cumene)	3Ⓨ E	Inflammable liquid
1919	Methyl acrylate, inhibited	3WE	Inflammable liquid
1920	Nonane and its isomers	3Ⓨ	Inflammable liquid
1942	Ammonium nitrate containing less than 0.2% of combustible substance	1Ⓣ	Oxidising substance
1969	Isobutane and isobutane mixtures	3WE	Inflammable gas
1976	Propane	3WE	Inflammable gas
2031	Nitric acid below 70%	2R	Corrosive
2032	Nitric acid above 70%	2P	Corrosive
2049	Diethylbenzene	3Ⓨ	Inflammable liquid

2050	Di-isobutylene, isomeric compounds (A–di-isobutylene, B–di-isobutylene, 2,4,4–Trimethyl pentene–1 2,4,4–Trimethyl pentene–2)	3Y E	Inflammable liquid
2052	Dipentene (Csjeputene; Cinene; di-paramenths–1, 8–dione; Limonene, inactive)	3Y	Inflammable liquid
2055	Styrene monomer, inhibited (Cinnamene, Cinnamel, Phenylethylene or Vinylbenzene)	3Y	Inflammable liquid
2056	Tetrahydrofuran	2SE	Inflammable liquid
2057	Tripopylene (Propylene trimer)	3Y	Inflammable liquid
2075	Ammonia solutions having a density (specific gravity) of less than 0.880 at 15°C in water, containing more than 35% and not above 50% ammonia	2PE	Toxic gas
2076	Cresole (ortho- meta- and para-)	2X	Poison
2222	Anisole	3Y	Inflammable liquid
2227	n-Butyl methacrylate	3Y	Inflammable liquid
2241	Cycloheptane	3Y E	Inflammable liquid
2242	Cycloheptane	3Y E	Inflammable liquid
2243	Cyclohexyl	3Y	Inflammable liquid
2245	Cyclopentanone	3Y	Inflammable liquid
2246	Cyclopentene	3Y E	Inflammable liquid
2247	n-Decane	3Y	Inflammable liquid
2256	Cyclohexane	3Y E	Inflammable liquid
2265	1-4 Dimethyl cyclohexane	3Y E	Inflammable liquid
2271	Ethyl iso amyl ketone	3Y	Inflammable liquid
2277	Ethyl methacrylate	3Y	Inflammable liquid
2278	n-Heptene	3Y E	Inflammable liquid

2284	Isobutyronitrile	3WE	Inflammable liquid
2287	Ischeptene	3☒ E	Inflammable liquid
2288	Isohexene	3☒ E	Inflammable liquid
2293	4-Methoxy-4-methyl-pentan-2-one	3Y	Inflammable liquid
2296	Methyl cyclohexane	3☒ E	Inflammable liquid
2297	Methyl cyclohexanone	3Y	Inflammable liquid
2298	Methyl cyclopentane	3☒ E	Inflammable liquid
2501	2-Methyl-Furan	3YE	Inflammable liquid
2302	5-Methyl Hexan-2-one	3Y	Inflammable liquid
2304	Napthalene (molten)	2X	Inflammable liquid
2305	Nitrobenzene Sulphonic Acid	2R	Corrosive
2312	Phenol (Carbolic acid) molten	2X	Poison
2334	Allyamine	2WE	Inflammable liquid
2370	Hex-I-one	3☒ E	Inflammable liquid
2447	Phosphorus white, molten	2WE	Spontaneously combustible
2448	Sulphur, molten	2X	Inflammable solid
2547	Sodium superoxide (Sodium Peroxide)	4W	Oxidising substance

Appendix 3

WIRE ROPE TABLE

6×19 (12/6/1)   100/110 tons in^2

Dia	Equivalent Circumference	BS (tons)	SWL (tons)	(Cwt)
$^5/_{16}$	1	3.3	0.66	13
$^3/_8$	$1^1/_8$	4.8	0.96	19
$^7/_{16}$	$1^3/_8$	6.5	1.30	26
$^1/_2$	$1^5/_8$	8.5	1.70	34
$^9/_{16}$	$1^3/_4$	10.7	2.14	43
$^5/_8$	2	13.2	2.64	53
$^{11}/_{16}$	$2^1/_8$	16.1	3.88	64
$^3/_4$	$2^3/_8$	19.0	3.80	76
$^{13}/_{16}$	$2^1/_2$	22.2	4.44	89
$^7/_8$	$2^3/_4$	25.5	5.10	108
$^{15}/_{16}$	3	29.5	5.90	
1	$3^1/_8$	33.5	6.70	
$1^1/_8$	$3^1/_2$	42.5	8.50	
$1^1/_4$	$3^7/_8$	52.5	10.50	
$1^3/_8$	$4^3/_8$	63.5	18.70	
$1^1/_2$	$4^3/_4$	75.5	15.10	

Appendix 4
CHASSIS SELECTOR CHART

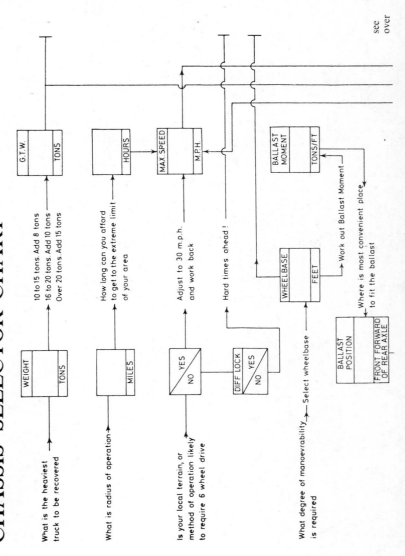

What is the heaviest truck to be recovered →

WEIGHT / TONS

10 to 15 tons. Add 8 tons
16 to 20 tons. Add 10 tons
Over 20 tons. Add 15 tons

G.T.W. / TONS

What is radius of operation →

MILES

How long can you afford to get to the extreme limit of your area

HOURS

Is your local terrain, or method of operation likely to require 6 wheel drive

YES / NO

Adjust to 30 m.p.h. and work back

MAX. SPEED / M.P.H.

DIFF LOCK — YES / NO

Hard times ahead !

What degree of manoevrability is required →

Select wheelbase →

WHEELBASE / FEET

→ Work out Ballast Moment

BALLAST MOMENT / TONS/FT

Where is most convenient place to fit the ballast

BALLAST POSITION / FRONT FORWARD OF REAR AXLE

see over

103

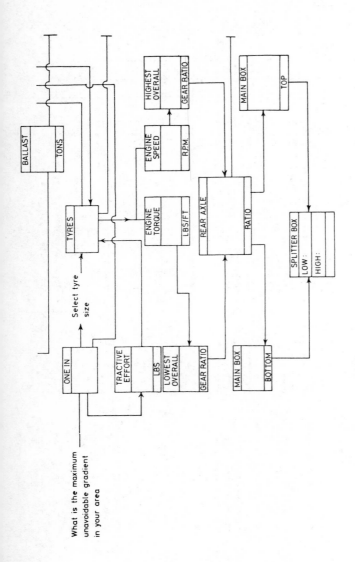

What is the maximum
unavoidable gradient
in your area

Select tyre
size

BALLAST

TONS

TYRES

ONE IN

TRACTIVE
EFFORT

LBS

LOWEST
OVERALL

GEAR RATIO

ENGINE
TORQUE

LBS/FT

ENGINE
SPEED

R.P.M.

HIGHEST
OVERALL

GEAR RATIO

REAR AXLE

RATIO

MAIN BOX

BOTTOM

MAIN BOX

TOP

SPLITTER BOX

LOW:

HIGH:

Appendix 5

USEFUL UNITS AND S.I. CONVERSION FACTORS

Abbreviations

m = metre
g = gramme
t = tonne (or metric ton)
N = newton (SI unit of force)
J = joule (SI unit of energy)
W = watt (SI unit of power)
s = second
M = mega (× 1 million)
k = kilo (× 1 thousand)
c = centi (1 hundredth)
m = milli (1 thousandth)
μ = micro (1 millionth)

Length

1 in = 25.4 mm
1 ft = 300 mm = 0.3 m (approx)
0.001 in = 0.0254 mm
1 mm = 0.03937 in
1 micron (μm) = 39.37 μin

Area

1 sq in (in^2) = 645.16 mm^2
　　　　　　 = 6.4516 cm^2
1 sq ft (ft^2) = 0.9 m^2
1 cm^2 = 0.155 in^2

Volume

1 cu in (in^3) = 16.387 cm^3
1 cu ft (ft^3) = 0.028 m^2
1 UK gal. = 4.546 litres
1 cm^3 = 0.061 in^3
1 litre = 1000 cm^3 = 61 in^3

Mass

1 lb = 0.4536 kg
1 ton = 1016 kg
1 kg = 2.205 lb
1 t = 1000 kg = 0.9842 ton

Force

1 lbf = 4.448 N
1 tonf = 9.964 kN
1 kgf = 9.807 N
1 N = 0.2248 lbf

Torque

1 pound-force foot (lbf ft)
　　　　　 = 1.356 N m
1 kgf m = 7.233 lbf ft
　　　　　 = 9.8067 N m
1 N m = 0.102 kgf m
　　　　　 = 0.7376 lbf ft

Pressure or stress

1 lbf/in^2 = 0.0703 kgf/cm^2
　　　　　 = 6.895 kN/m^2
1 tonf/in^2 = 1.575 kgf/mm^2
　　　　　 = 15.444 MN/m^2
1 kgf/cm^2 = 14.223 lbf/in^2
　　　　　 = 98.067 kN/m^2
1 N/m^2 = 0.000145 lbf/in^2
(pascal)
1 bar = 14.50377 lbf/in^2
　　　　　 = 10^5 N/m^2

Energy (work, heat)

1 ft lbf = 0.1383 kgf in = 1.356 J
1 Btu = 1.055 kJ
1 kJ = 102 kgf m = 737.6 ft lbf

Power

1 horsepower (hp) = 550 ft lbf/s
　　　　　 = 1.0139 metric hp
　　　　　 = 76.04 kgf m/s
　　　　　 = 745.7 W
1 metric hp = 75 kgf m/s
　　　　　 = 735.5 W
1 ft lbf/s = 0.1383 kgf m/s
　　　　　 = 1.356 W
1 watt = 0.7376 ft lbf/s
　　　　　 = 0.102 kgf m/s
　　　　　 = 1 J/s = 1 N m/s
1 kW = 1.341 hp
　　　　　 = 1.36 metric hp

INDEX

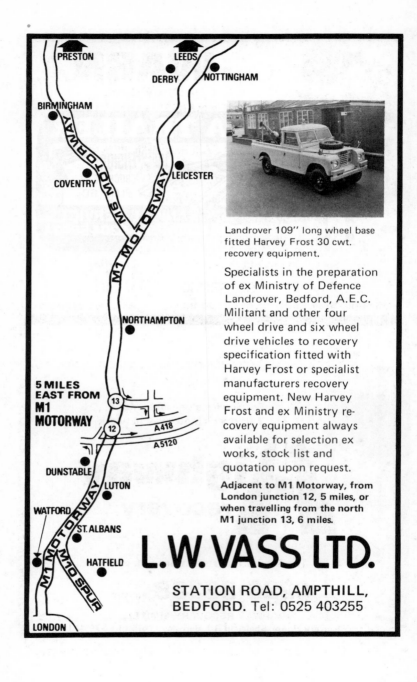

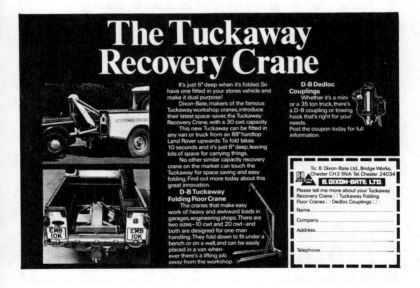

Lucas emergency lighting
Far safer, more efficient.
Simply the best...

A complete range of emergency lighting equipment that's specifically designed to meet every kind of accident recovery situation.

Lucas beacon lamps are used by police, ambulance, and GPO in the UK. They are super efficient and will help you provide a far safer, more efficient breakdown service.

A magnetic fixing base which allows beacon lamps to be fixed temporarily to the roofs of steel-bodied vehicles is also included in the range.

Also available are Lucas worklamps which, utilising either tungsten or halogen light sources, greatly assist night-time recovery work.

Visit your local Lucas Service agent (there are over 300 throughout the UK), and see the complete range of emergency lighting by Europe's foremost electrical equipment manufacturer. You'll find the one nearest you listed in 'Yellow Pages' under Garage Services.